GRAPHS AND THEIR USES

NEW MATHEMATICAL LIBRARY

published by
Random House and The L. W. Singer Company
for the
Monograph Project
of the
SCHOOL MATHEMATICS STUDY GROUP†

EDITORIAL PANEL

† The School Mathematics Study Group represents all parts of the mathematical profession and all parts of the country. Its activities are aimed at the
improvement of teaching of mathematics in our schools. Further information
can be obtained from: School Mathematics Study Group, School
of Education, Stanford University, Stanford, California.

GRAPHS AND THEIR USES

by

Oystein Ore

Yale University

10
RANDOM HOUSE

Illustrations by Ruth Kessler

First Printing

Library of Congress Catalog-Card Number: 63–9345

Manufactured in the United States of America

Note to the Reader

This book is one of a series written by professional mathematicians in order to make some important mathematical ideas interesting and understandable to a large audience of high school students and laymen. Most of the volumes in the *New Mathematical Library* cover topics not usually included in the high school curriculum; they vary in difficulty, and, even within a single book, some parts require a greater degree of concentration than others. Thus, while the reader needs little technical knowledge to understand most of these books, he will have to make an intellectual effort.

If the reader has so far encountered mathematics only in classroom work, he should keep in mind that a book on mathematics cannot be read quickly. Nor must he expect to understand all parts of the book on first reading. He should feel free to skip complicated parts and return to them later; often an argument will be clarified by a subsequent remark. On the other hand, sections containing thoroughly familiar material may be read very quickly.

The best way to learn mathematics is to *do* mathematics, and each book includes problems, some of which may require considerable thought. The reader is urged to acquire the habit of reading with paper and pencil in hand; in this way mathematics will become increasingly meaningful to him.

For the authors and editors this is a new venture. They wish to acknowledge the generous help given them by the many high school teachers and students who assisted in the preparation of these monographs. The editors are interested in reactions to the books in this series and hope that readers will write to: Editorial Committee of the NML series, in care of THE INSTITUTE OF MATHEMATICAL SCIENCES, NEW YORK UNIVERSITY, New York 3, N. Y.

The Editors

NEW MATHEMATICAL LIBRARY

Other titles will be announced as ready

Contents

GRAPHS AND THEIR USES

INTRODUCTION

The term "graph" in this book denotes something quite different from the graphs you may be familiar with from analytic geometry or function theory. The kind of graph you probably have dealt with consisted of the set of all points in the plane whose coordinates (x, y), in some coordinate system, satisfy an equation in x and y. The graphs we are about to study in this book are simple geometrical figures consisting of points and lines connecting some of these points; they are sometimes called "linear graphs". It is unfortunate that two different concepts bear the same name, but this terminology is now so well established that it would be difficult to change. Similar ambiguities in the names of things appear in other mathematical fields, and unless there is danger of serious confusion, mathematicians are reluctant to alter the terminology.

The first paper on graph theory was written by the famous Swiss mathematician Euler and appeared in 1736. From a mathematical point of view, the theory of graphs seemed rather insignificant in the beginning since it dealt largely with entertaining puzzles. But recent developments in mathematics and particularly in its applications have given a strong impetus to graph theory. Already in the nineteenth century graphs were used in such fields as electrical circuitry and molecular diagrams. At present there are topics in pure mathematics, for instance, the theory of mathematical relations, where graph theory is a natural tool, but there are also numerous other uses in connection with highly practical questions: matchings, transportation problems, the flow in pipe line networks, and so-called "programming" in general. Graph theory now makes its appearance in such diverse fields as economics, psychology and biology.

3

To a small extent puzzles remain a part of graph theory, particularly if one includes among them the famous *four color map conjecture* that intrigues mathematicians today as much as ever.

In mathematics graph theory is classified as a branch of topology; but it is also strongly related to algebra and matrix theory.

In the following discussion we have been compelled to treat only some of the simplest problems from graph theory; we have selected these with the intention of giving an impression, on the one hand, of the kind of analyses that can be made by means of graphs and, on the other hand, of some of the problems that can be attacked by such methods. Fortunately, no great apparatus of mathematical computations needs to be introduced.

CHAPTER ONE

What is a Graph?

1.1 Team Competitions

Suppose that your school football team belongs to a league in which it plays the teams of certain other schools. Call your own team A and the other teams B, C, D, E and F, and assume that there are 6 teams altogether. After a few weeks of the season have passed some of the teams will have played each other, for instance,

A has played C, D, F
B has played C, E, F
C has played A, B
D has played A, E, F
E has played B, D, F
F has played A, B, D, E.

To illustrate this situation one can use a geometric diagram. Each team can be represented by a point or a little circle, and two such points can be connected by a straight line whenever the teams they represent have played their game. Then the above list of completed games can be presented as in Figure 1.1.1.

A figure such as the one drawn in Figure 1.1.1 is called a *graph*. It consists of certain points A, B, C, D, E, F, called its *vertices* and certain line segments connecting vertices, such as AC, EB, etc., called the *edges* of the graph.

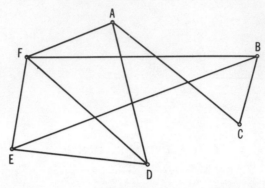

Figure 1.1.1

It may happen, as one sees from Figure 1.1.1, that the edges of a graph intersect without the intersection being a vertex; this complication is due to the fact that we drew our graph in the plane. Therefore, it might have been more appropriate to represent the edges as threads passing over each other in space; but in any case the marking of the vertices should be done with sufficient care to prevent confusion.

Any set of games played in a team tournament can be depicted as a graph in the manner described. On the other hand if one has some graph, that is, a figure consisting of points or vertices connected by line segments or edges, then it can be interpreted as the diagram of such a competition. As an illustration let us take the graph drawn in Figure 1.1.2. The figure may be considered to depict a competition between 8 teams; A has played with the teams B, E, D, while B has played with A, F, G, C, and so on.

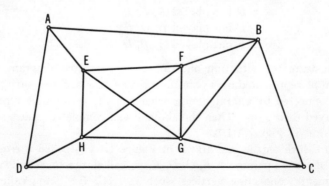

Figure 1.1.2

Problem Set 1.1

1. Draw the graph of the games played at mid-season in your football or baseball circuit.

2. Write a complete list of the games played in the graph in Figure 1.1.2.

3. How many edges and vertices are there in the graphs in Figure 1.1.1 and Figure 1.1.2 respectively?

1.2 Null Graphs and Complete Graphs

There are certain special graphs which turn up in many uses of graph theory. For the moment let us stick to our interpretation of a graph as a pictorial record of team competitions. Before the season starts, when no games have been played, there will be no edges in the graph. Thus the graph will consist only of *isolated vertices*, that is, vertices at which there are no edges. We call a graph of this kind a *null graph*. In Figure 1.2.1 we have drawn such graphs for 1, 2, 3, 4 and 5 teams or vertices. These null graphs are commonly denoted by the symbols O_1, O_2, O_3, and so on, so that in general O_n is the null graph with n vertices and no edges.

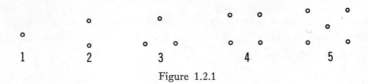

Figure 1.2.1

Next let us go to another extreme. When the season is over we suppose that each team has played just once with every other team. Then in the game graph each pair of vertices is connected by an edge. Such a graph is called a *complete graph* (sometimes a *universal graph*). Figure 1.2.2 shows the complete graphs for $n = 1, 2, 3, 4, 5$ vertices. We denote these complete graphs by U_1, U_2, U_3, U_4, U_5, respectively, so that in general U_n consists of n vertices and the edges connecting all pairs of these vertices. It can be drawn as a polygon with n sides and with all its diagonals.

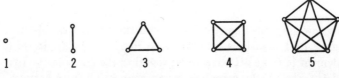

Figure 1.2.2

When one has drawn some graph, for instance the graph G in Figure 1.1.1, one can always make it into a complete graph with the same vertices by adding the missing edges, that is, the edges which correspond to games still to be played. In Figure 1.2.3 we have done this for the graph G in Figure 1.1.1. (Games not yet played are represented by broken lines.)

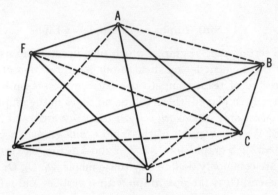

Figure 1.2.3

One can also draw separately the graph consisting exclusively of the unplayed, future games. In the case of graph G, this results in the graph depicted in Figure 1.2.4.

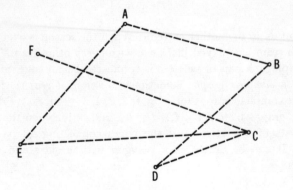

Figure 1.2.4

This new graph in Figure 1.2.4 we call the *complement* of the graph G in Figure 1.1.1, and it is customary to denote it by $\bar{G}$. If we take the complement of $\bar{G}$ we get back to G; together the edges in the two graphs G and $\bar{G}$ make up the complete graph connecting their vertices.

1. Draw the complement of the graph in Figure 1.1.2.

2. Express in terms of n the number of edges in a complete graph U_n.

1.3 Isomorphic Graphs

Notice that in drawing the graph in Figure 1.1.1 we have a good deal of freedom.

First, there is no necessity for the edges to be straight lines. Any kind of curves will do as long as they connect the same vertices as before. For example, we can present the graph in Figure 1.1.1 in the following shape (Figure 1.3.1):

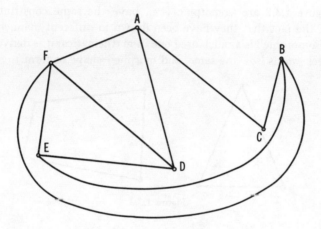

Figure 1.3.1

Secondly, we can place the vertices in arbitrary positions in the plane. The graph in Figure 1.1.1, for instance, can be drawn with the vertices placed as in Figure 1.3.2.

If we consider the three graphs in Figure 1.1.1, Figure 1.3.1 and Figure 1.3.2 as the graphs of tournament games, they all contain exactly the same information in regard to which teams have played each other; that is, they are in a sense the same graph. This leads us to say in general that two graphs, call them G_1 and G_2, are *isomorphic* if they are the images of the same situation. In other words, if G_1 and G_2 are isomorphic they have the same number of vertices, and whenever two vertices in G_1, say (B_1, C_1), are connected by an edge, then there are corresponding vertices (B_2, C_2) in G_2 also connected by an edge, and vice versa. According to this definition the three graphs in Figure 1.1.1, Figure 1.3.1,

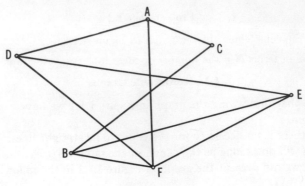

Figure 1.3.2

and Figure 1.3.2 are isomorphic (i.e., have the same constitution) in spite of the fact that they have been drawn in different manners. (The term "isomorphic" is a much used one in mathematics; it is derived from the Greek words iso—the same, and morphe—shape or form.)

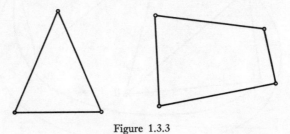

Figure 1.3.3

Often one is faced with the problem of deciding whether two graphs are isomorphic. At times there are obvious reasons why this cannot be the case. For example, the graphs in Figure 1.3.3 cannot be isomorphic because they do not have the same number of vertices. Nor can the graphs in Figure 1.3.4 be isomorphic, since they do not have the same number of edges.

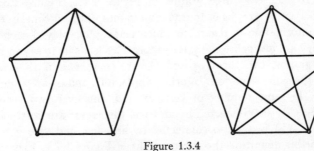

Figure 1.3.4

Slightly more subtle reasoning is required to show that the two graphs in Figure 1.3.5 are not isomorphic. One can observe, however, that in the first graph there is a sequence of 8 adjoining edges (edges having a common vertex)

$$(1, 2), (2, 3), (3, 4), (4, 8), (8, 7), (7, 6), (6, 5), (5, 1)$$

returning to the initial vertex, while in the second graph there is no such sequence. In other words, no matter how we name the vertices of the second graph, we shall not be able to match pairs of vertices connected by an edge in one graph with corresponding pairs of vertices connected by an edge in the other graph. (Verify this!)

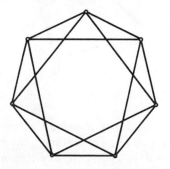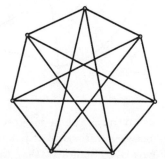

Figure 1.3.5

When there is no obvious way to show that two graphs are not isomorphic it may be quite difficult to decide whether one can name the vertices in such a manner that one obtains an isomorphism between the graphs. As an example, we propose the two graphs in Figure 1.3.6; they are actually isomorphic.

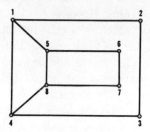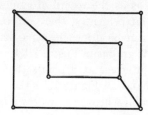

Figure 1.3.6

Problem Set 1.3

1. Show that the graphs in Figure 1.1.1, Figure 1.1.2 and Figure 1.2.4 are not isomorphic to each other.

2. Give another reason why the two graphs in Figure 1.3.5 cannot be isomorphic.

3. Name the vertices in the two graphs in Figure 1.3.6 so that their isomorphism becomes evident.

1.4 Planar Graphs

For many purposes it does not matter how a graph is drawn; that is, isomorphic graphs may be considered to be the same since they give the same information. This was certainly the case in our initial interpretation of graphs as the record of games between teams. However, as we shall point out presently, there are purposes for which it is essential that a graph can be drawn in a particular way. Let us compare the two isomorphic graphs in Figure 1.1.1 and Figure 1.3.1. In the first drawing the edges intersect at 5 points that are not vertices of the graph. On the other hand, in Figure 1.3.1 the edges intersect only at vertices.

A graph which can be drawn in such a way that the edges have no intersections or common points except at the vertices is called a *planar graph*. Thus the graph in Figure 1.1.1 is planar because there exists a representation of it in the plane as in Figure 1.3.1.

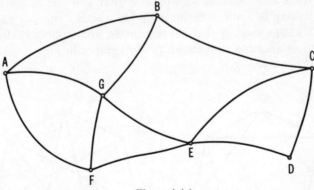

Figure 1.4.1

A planar graph can be interpreted as a road map showing the connections between various road junctions or villages. For instance, the map in Figure 1.4.1 indicates that there are 7 junctions, A to G, some of which are directly connected by roads, e.g. (A, G), (B, C), (F, E), and so on. Conversely, a road map can be considered to be a planar graph.

Similarly a city map is a planar graph with the streets as edges and the squares or street intersections as vertices; see Figure 1.4.2.

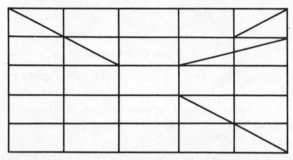

Figure 1.4.2

Modern technology has changed many things and, to be quite up to date, we must recognize that it has modified also the preceding simple conception of road maps as planar graphs. To our road net have been added throughways with limited access so that often two roads cross without permitting passage from one to the other; in other words, the edges of the map graph intersect at points which are not road junctions.

Figure 1.4.3

Problem Set 1.4

1. From an automobile map draw a planar road graph for a certain section of your state.

2. Do the same for a city map.

1.5 Planar Problems

We shall now consider two instances of the use of graphs in problem solving. In both cases it is essential to decide whether or not a graph can be drawn in the plane without intersections of the edges. As our first illustration let us turn to a very ancient puzzle (sometimes called the *Utility Problem*):

Three houses have been built on a piece of land and three wells have been dug for the use of the occupants. The nature of the land and the climate is such that one or another of the wells frequently runs dry; it is therefore important that the people of each house have access to each of the three wells. After a while the residents *A*, *B* and *C* develop rather strong dislikes of one another and decide to construct paths to the three wells *X*, *Y*, *Z* in such a manner that they avoid meeting each other on their way to and from the wells.

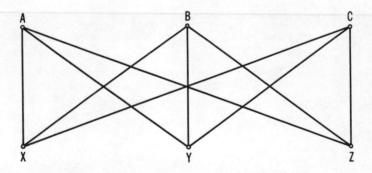

Figure 1.5.1

In Figure 1.5.1 one sees the graph of the natural arrangement in which each owner uses the most direct paths to the wells. These paths or edges intersect in many points aside from the houses *A*, *B*, *C*, and the wells *X*, *Y*, *Z*. The number of intersections can be reduced to a single one provided one draws the paths as indicated in Figure 1.5.2.

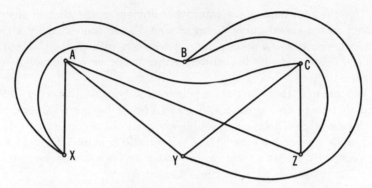

Figure 1.5.2

The question we should like to have answered is the following: Can one trace the paths so that the graph is planar, that is, without any edge intersections? Try as you may, you will find no such tracing. However, our inability to solve this problem by trial and error does not constitute a mathematical proof that no such tracing exists. A mathematical proof can be given and is based on the

JORDAN CURVE THEOREM. *Suppose K is a continuous closed curve in the plane; it may be a polygon, a circle, an ellipse, or some more complicated type of curve. Then K divides the plane into an outer and an inner part so that whenever any point P in the inner part is connected to a point Q in the outer part by a continuous curve L, then L intersects K.* (See Figure 1.5.3. You probably feel that this is perfectly obvious, and, from an intuitive geometric view, it is. The difficulty lies in the precise definition of "curve", which we omit here together with the proof of Jordan's theorem. You may take the theorem as an evident fact.)

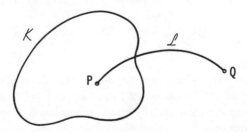

Figure 1.5.3

This theorem implies the intuitively obvious result that if any two points on the closed curve K, say A and Y, are connected by a curve (A, Y) which has no other points in common with K, then, except for its end points, (A, Y) lies entirely either inside or outside of K. (See Figure 1.5.4.)

Suppose next that there are 4 points on K lying in the order $ABYZ$ and that there are curves (A, Y) and (B, Z) having no intersections with each other. This is only possible when one of the curves, say (A, Y), lies inside K while the other, (B, Z), is outside (Figure 1.5.4). This can be proved by Jordan's theorem, but you may (as we have done) take it as a fact that needs no further justification.

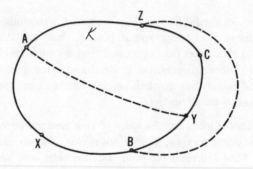

Figure 1.5.4

Finally, let there be 6 points on K following in the order (Figure 1.5.4)

$$A, X, B, Y, C, Z.$$

Then it is impossible that there are three connecting curves

$$(A, Y), \quad (B, Z) \quad (C, X)$$

without intersections.

To see this, observe that three curves must be placed into two regions, the inside of K and the outside of K; therefore at least two of the curves fall into the same region and by the considerations above, this would lead to intersections.

This argument applies immediately to our problem of the three bad neighbors and their wells. Suppose that the corresponding graph in

Figure 1.5.1 were planar. Then in the drawing without edge intersections the edges

$$(A, X), (X, B), (B, Y), (Y, C), (C, Z), (Z, A)$$

would form a closed curve in the plane. But then for the reason we just explained there can be no edges

$$(A, Y), \quad (B, Z), \quad (C, X)$$

without intersections.

This illustration of the use of planar graphs may seem somewhat trivial; however, one should never despise these apparently small, but puzzling problems. They have in numerous instances been the seeds from which important mathematical ideas have evolved. It may remind us also that a heavy machinery of symbols and formulas is not always the best criterion for judging the depth of a mathematical theory.

Let us indicate an application of planar graphs to an eminently practical problem. In addition to the previous interpretations of a graph we may mention that it can be thought of as the diagram for an electrical network, with the edges representing the conducting wires connecting the various junctions. One of the most effective ways of mass producing a standard network for a radio or television set is to print the wires by means of metal foil on a base of paper board or plastic. But in order for this to be feasible the network graph in question must have a planar representation; otherwise the intersection of two edges would produce a short circuit in the system.

Problem Set 1.5

Each of four neighbors has connected his house with the other three houses by paths which do not cross. A fifth man builds a house nearby.

1. Prove that he cannot connect his house with all the others by non-intersecting paths.

2. Show that he can connect it with three of the others.

1.6 The Number of Edges in a Graph

In introducing a graph as the record of a series of played games we assumed that at most one game was played between any two teams. It may of course happen that two teams play many games, as they do in the baseball leagues. We can take this into account in the graph by drawing several edges (A, B) connecting the two corresponding teams or vertices (Figure 1.6.1). We then say that the graph has *multiple edges*.

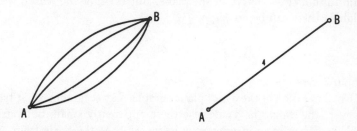

Figure 1.6.1

Instead of actually drawing the various edges between A and B one could also use a single edge and assign a number or *multiplicity* to it to indicate how many times this edge should be repeated (Figure 1.6.1). On a road map it is of course customary to draw each road separately between the two junctions.

At each non-isolated vertex A in a graph G there will be some edges having A as an endpoint; these edges are said to be *incident* to A. The number of such edges we usually denote by $\rho(A)$ and call it the *local degree* at A. To illustrate, we observe that the graph in Figure 1.1.1 has the local degrees

$$\rho(A) = \rho(B) = \rho(D) = \rho(E) = 3, \qquad \rho(F) = 4, \qquad \rho(C) = 2.$$

For many purposes we are interested in finding the number of edges in the graph. They can of course be counted directly, but it is often easier to count the number of edges at each vertex and add them. Then each edge has been counted twice, once at each of its two end points, so the number of edges in the graph is half this sum. For instance, the number of edges in the graph in Figure 1.1.1 is

$$\tfrac{1}{2}[\rho(A) + \rho(B) + \rho(C) + \rho(D) + \rho(E) + \rho(F)] = 9,$$

as one also sees directly.

To formulate this quite generally assume that G is a graph with the n vertices

$$A_1, A_2, \cdots, A_n$$

having for their local degrees the numbers

$$\rho(A_1), \quad \rho(A_2), \quad \cdots, \quad \rho(A_n).$$

Then the number N of edges in G is, by our argument,

(1.6.1) $$N = \tfrac{1}{2}[\rho(A_1) + \cdots + \rho(A_n)].$$

This formula has the consequence that *in any graph the sum of the local degrees*

(1.6.2) $$\sum_{i=1}^{n} \rho(A_i) = \rho(A_1) + \cdots + \rho(A_n)$$

is an even number, namely twice the number of edges.

In a graph there are two types of vertices, the *odd vertices* A' for which the local degree $\rho(A')$ is an odd number and the *even vertices* A'' for which $\rho(A'')$ is an even number. Again in the case of the graph in Figure 1.1.1 the vertices A, B, D, E are odd while the vertices C and F are even. When the vertices are taken in alphabetical order the sum (1.6.2) becomes

$$3 + 3 + 2 + 3 + 3 + 4 = 18.$$

This sum is even for there are 4 terms which are odd numbers.

To decide in general whether a sum of integers is odd or even we can disregard the even terms; the sum is even or odd depending upon whether it contains an even or an odd number of odd summands. When we apply this observation to the fact that the sum (1.6.2) is even we arrive at the following:

THEOREM 1.1. *A graph has an even number of odd vertices.*

We include in this statement the case where there are no odd vertices, since 0 is an even number.

There are special graphs in which all local degrees are the same:

$$\rho(A_1) = \cdots = \rho(A_n) = r.$$

The graph is then called *regular of degree r* and according to the formula (1.6.1) the number of its edges is

$$N = \tfrac{1}{2}nr,$$

where n is the number of its vertices. The graphs in Figure 1.6.2 are regular of degree 3 and 4 respectively.

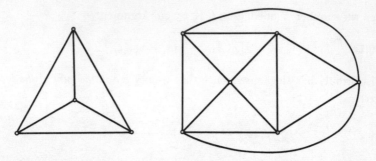

Figure 1.6.2

In a complete graph U_n with n vertices there are $n - 1$ edges from each vertex to the others so that U_n is regular of degree $n - 1$. The null graph O_n is also regular in a trivial way since $\rho(A) = 0$ for each vertex.

Problem Set 1.6

1. Check the formula (1.6.1) for the number of edges in the graphs in Figure 1.1.2 and Figure 1.2.4.

2. Verify that for these graphs the number of odd vertices is even.

CHAPTER TWO

Connected Graphs

2.1 The Components

Assume again that we have a graph G, not necessarily planar, which we shall think of now as a road map. We may then begin a trip in G at some vertex A, following first an edge or road (A, B) to some junction B, then from B to C on another connecting road (B, C), and so on. We shall place no restriction on our meandering along the roads; we may pass the same place several times and even use the same roads over again.

If on this trip we arrive at some vertex T we say that T is *connected* to A in the graph. This means that there are roads leading from A to T. If we have passed the same locality more than once we can eliminate a circular route and make the trip from A to T more direct. A route in G that passes no vertices twice is called an *arc*; the route in Figure 2.1.1 is an arc.

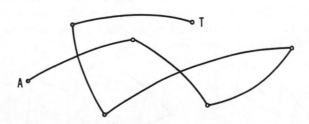

Figure 2.1.1

21

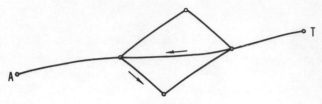

Figure 2.1.2

A sightseeing route passing the same vertices several times but never using the same piece of road over again is called a *path* (Figure 2.1.2). If the path returns to the starting point we call it *cyclic* or *circular*, while a returning arc is called a *circuit*. Thus a cyclic path may intersect itself at some of the vertices, but in a cyclic arc only the starting vertex is re-visited, as end point.

Let us illustrate these concepts on the graph in Figure 1.1.1. The edge sequence

$$ADFEB$$

is an arc; the sequence

$$AFDEFB$$

is a path. A cyclic path is represented by

$$AFEDFBCA$$

while

$$ACBFEDA$$

is a circuit.

When every vertex in a graph is connected to every other vertex by an arc we say the graph is *connected*. All graphs we have used as illustrations are connected except the null graphs. If a graph is not connected one cannot reach all vertices by arcs from any given vertex A. Those vertices that can be reached by arcs from a vertex A, and the edges incident to them, we call the *connected component* of A. In this manner the whole graph falls into connected components with no edges or arcs connecting the separate components.

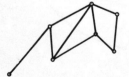

Figure 2.1.3

In Figure 2.1.3 we have illustrated a graph with 4 connected components, one of them an isolated vertex. From the map point of view one may consider it the road graph of islands, each island having a connected road system. For many considerations in graph theory one can suppose that the graph is connected since one can examine separately the properties of each connected component.

2.2 The Problem of the Bridges in Königsberg

The theory of graphs is one of the few fields of mathematics with a definite birth date. The first paper on graphs was written by the Swiss mathematician Leonhard Euler (1707–1783) and it appeared in the 1736 volume of the publications of the Academy of Science in St. Petersburg (Leningrad). Euler is one of the most impressive figures in the history of science. In 1727, when he was 20 years old, he was invited to the Russian academy. He had already studied theology, oriental languages and medicine before he gave free rein to his interests in mathematics, physics, and astronomy. His skill in all these fields was great, and his productivity was enormous. About the time he wrote the paper on graphs he lost his sight in one eye, and as an older man he became totally blind; but even this did not slow the flow of his writings. A considerable time ago Swiss mathematicians, particularly those of his native town of Basel, began an edition of Euler's complete works and 50 volumes have appeared so far. The original estimate of the number of books his writings would fill ran to about 100, but at present it seems that 200 is a more likely estimate.

Euler began his paper on graphs by discussing a puzzle, the so-called *Königsberg Bridge Problem*. The city of Königsberg (now Kaliningrad) in East Prussia is located on the banks and on two islands of the river Pregel. The various parts of the city were connected by seven bridges.

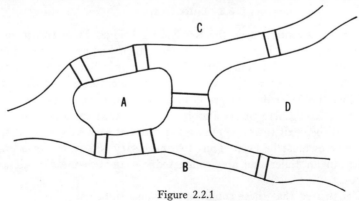

Figure 2.2.1

On Sundays the burghers would take their promenade around town, as is usual in German cities. The problem arose: Is it possible to plan this "Spaziergang" in such a manner that, starting from home, one can return there after having crossed each river bridge just once?

A schematic map of Königsberg is reproduced in Figure 2.2.1. The four parts of the city are denoted by the letters A, B, C and D. Since we are interested only in the bridge crossings we may think of A, B, C, D as the vertices of a graph with connecting edges corresponding to the bridges. This graph is drawn in Figure 2.2.2.

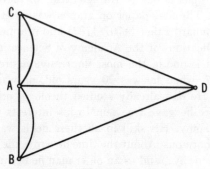

Figure 2.2.2

Euler showed that this graph cannot be traversed completely in a single circular path; in other words, no matter at which vertex one begins, one cannot cover the graph and come back to the starting point without retracing one's steps. Such a path would have to enter each vertex as many times as it departs from it; hence it requires an even number of edges at each vertex, and this condition is not fulfilled in the graph representing the map of Königsberg.

2.3 Euler Graphs

After his introduction on the Königsberg bridges Euler turned in his paper to the general graph problem: In which graphs is it possible to find a cyclic path ρ running through all edges just once? Such a path is now called an *Euler line* and a graph with an Euler line is an *Euler graph*.

To have an Euler line the graph must be connected. As in the discussion of the Königsberg Bridge Problem one sees that any Euler line must enter and then exit the same number of times at each vertex, that is, all local degrees must be even. Thus two necessary conditions for a graph to contain an Euler line are: connectedness and evenness of all local degrees.

Euler proved that these conditions are also sufficient.

THEOREM 2.1. *A connected graph with even local degrees has an Euler line.*

PROOF. Suppose that we begin a path $\mathcal{L}$ at some vertex A and continue it as far as possible, always departing from a vertex on an edge which we have not traversed before. The process must stop after a while since we shall run out of new edges. But since there is an even number of edges at each vertex there is always an exit except at the initial vertex A. Thus $\mathcal{L}$ must come to a halt at A. (See Figure 2.3.1.)

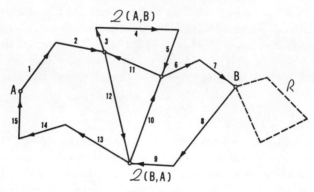

Figure 2.3.1

If $\mathcal{L}$ passes through all edges we have obtained an Euler line as we wanted. If not there will be some vertex B lying on $\mathcal{L}$ where there are edges not traversed by $\mathcal{L}$. As a matter of fact, since $\mathcal{L}$ has an even number of edges at B there must be an even number of edges at B which do not belong to $\mathcal{L}$ and the same must be true for all vertices where there are untraversed edges.

We now start a path $\mathcal{R}$ from B, this time using only edges not in $\mathcal{L}$. Again the path must finally come to a halt at B. But then we have gained a larger cyclic path from A obtained by following $\mathcal{L}$ in a path $\mathcal{L}(A, B)$ to B, then taking the cyclic path $\mathcal{R}$ and returning to B, and finally following the remaining part $\mathcal{L}(B, A)$ of $\mathcal{L}$ back to A. (See Figure 2.3.1). If we still have not covered the whole graph we can enlarge the path again and so on until we actually have an Euler line.

The drawing of Euler lines is an entertainment familiar to those who work the puzzles in children's magazines. The members of the youngest set are enticed to find out how a picture of some kind can be drawn in one continuous line without repetitions and without lifting the pencil from the paper.

Instead of restricting oneself to cyclic paths, one often drops the condition that the path covering all edges shall return to the initial point.

When there exists a path $\mathcal{2}(A, B)$ starting at A and ending in another vertex, B, and passing once through all edges, then $\mathcal{2}$ must depart from the vertex A on some edge and possibly reenter and redepart from A a number of times. If this path does not end at A, then the vertex A must be odd. For an analogous reason B is odd while all other vertices must be even. This yields the

THEOREM 2.2. *A connected graph has a path $\mathcal{2}(A, B)$ covering all edges just once if and only if A and B are the only odd vertices.*

The proof follows from the fact that one can add a new edge (A, B) so that all vertices become even. The new graph has an Euler line ρ by the previous theorem, and when the edge (A, B) is dropped from ρ the remaining path is $\mathcal{2}(A, B)$. As an example one may take the graph in Figure 1.2.4 which has just two odd vertices F and C and the covering path

$$FCDBAEC.$$

Mathematicians are forever searching for generalizations of the results they have already found. In this spirit let us try to determine for a general graph the smallest number of paths such that no two of them have a common edge and all these paths together cover the entire graph. If there is such a family of paths in a graph, we notice that every odd vertex must be the starting point or the end-point of at least one of them, for otherwise the vertex would have to be even. As we saw in Section 1.6 the number of odd vertices was even, say $2k$. Thus according to what we just stated any family of paths $\mathcal{2}$ covering the edges must include at least k paths. We show next that the number $2k$ of odd vertices is sufficient for k paths.

THEOREM 2.3. *A connected graph with $2k$ odd vertices contains a family of k distinct paths which, together, traverse all edges of the graph exactly once.*

PROOF. Let the odd vertices in the graph be denoted by

$$A_1, \quad A_2, \quad \cdots, \quad A_k; \qquad B_1, \quad B_2, \quad \cdots, \quad B_k$$

in some order. When we add the k edges

$$(A_1, B_1), \quad (A_2, B_2), \quad \cdots, \quad (A_k, B_k)$$

to the graph all vertices become even and there is an Euler line ρ. When these edges are dropped out again ρ falls into k separate paths covering the edges in the original graph.

As an example one may take the graph in Figure 1.1.1. It has 4 odd vertices, namely A, B, D, E, and is covered by the two paths

$$EBFA, \qquad BCADFED.$$

Problem Set 2.3

1. Determine how many paths are necessary to cover the graphs in Figure 2.3.2.

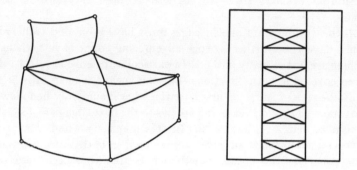

Figure 2.3.2

2. Do the same for all graphs used as illustrations in the preceding pages.

3. Determine covering paths for the universal graphs with 4 and 5 vertices. Try to generalize.

2.4 Finding Your Way

An Euler graph would be a suitable plan for an exposition, for here one can indicate by signs along the roads how the public should move in order to pass each exhibit once. But suppose that, as usual, the show is so arranged that there are exhibits on both sides of the ways. Then it is possible without any restrictions on the graph (except connectedness, of course) to guide the visitor in such a manner that each road is traversed twice, once in each direction.

To verify this we shall describe a general rule for constructing a route that passes along all edges of a graph just once in each direction. We begin our walk along some edge $\mathcal{E}_0 = (A_0, A_1)$ from an arbitrary vertex A_0. We mark this edge with a little arrow at A_0 to indicate which direction we have taken. We proceed successively to other vertices; the same vertex may be visited several times. At A_1 and each time later when a vertex is reached one leaves an arrow on the edge to indicate the direction of arrival. In addition, the first time one arrives at a new vertex one marks the entering edge specially so that it can be recognized later.

From each vertex one always exits along unused directions, either along edges which have not previously been traversed or along edges which have been marked as arrival edges; only when there are no other choices is it permissible to use the first entering edge as an exit.

We continue this winding way as far as it is possible. At any vertex there are just as many possibilities for an exit as for an entry. As a consequence the process can stop only at the initial vertex A_0. It remains to establish that at all vertices all edges have been traversed in both directions.

At A_0 this is simple, for all exit edges must have been used (otherwise we could have gone further), hence all entering edges have been used since there are just as many of these. In particular the edge $\mathcal{E}_0 = (A_0, A_1)$ has been covered in both directions. But this means that all exits at A_1 have also been used since the first entering edge should only be followed as a last resort. The same reasoning applies to the next edge $\mathcal{E}_1 = (A_1, A_2)$ and the next vertex A_2 and so on. In this manner we find that at all vertices we have reached all edges are covered in both ways. Since our graph is connected this means that the whole graph has been traversed.

This method of passing through all edges of a graph may be used for many purposes. It may be used for finding a way out of a maze or a labyrinth, and should you by chance be lost in a cave you may give it a try.

Problem Set 2.4

1. Apply the preceding method to the graphs illustrated in Section 1.1.

2.5   Hamilton Lines

In the year 1859 the famous Irish mathematician Sir William Rowan Hamilton put on the market a peculiar puzzle. Its main part was a *regular dodecahedron* made of wood (Figure 2.5.1). This is one of the so-called *regular Platonic bodies*, a polyhedron having regular pentagons for its 12 faces, with three edges of these pentagons meeting at each of the 20 corners.

Each corner of Hamilton's dodecahedron was marked with the name of an important city: Brussels, Canton, Delhi, Frankfurt, and so on. The puzzle consisted in finding a travel route along the edges of the dodecahedron which passed through each city just once; a few of the first cities to be visited should be stipulated in advance to render the task more challenging. To make it easier to remember which passages had already been completed each corner of the dodecahedron was provided with a nail with a large head, so that a string could be wound around the nails as the journey progressed. The dodecahedron was cumbersome to maneuver so that Hamilton also produced a version of his game in which the poly-hedron was replaced by a planar graph isomorphic to the graph formed by the edges of the dodecahedron (Figure 2.5.2).

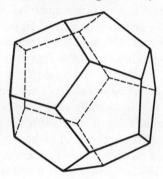

Figure 2.5.1

There is no indication that the Traveller's Dodecahedron had any great public success, but mathematicians have preserved a permanent memento of the puzzle: A *Hamilton line* in a graph is a circuit that passes through each of the vertices exactly once. It does not, in general, cover all the edges; in fact, it covers only two edges at each vertex. The circuit drawn in Figure 2.5.2 is a Hamilton line for the dodecahedron.

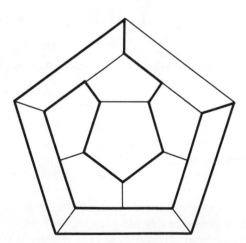

Figure 2.5.2

There is, as one sees, a certain analogy between the Euler lines and the Hamilton lines. In the former one should pass each edge once, in the latter, each vertex once. In spite of this resemblance the two problems represent entirely different degrees of difficulty. For an Euler graph it was sufficient to examine whether all vertices were even; for Hamilton lines mathematicians have found no such general criterion. This is regrettable since there are many important questions in graph theory which depend on the existence or non-existence of Hamilton lines.

The *Travelling Salesman's Problem* is a problem in the field of operations research which is reminiscent of the Hamilton lines; again we know of no general method of solution. Suppose that a travelling salesman is obliged to visit a number of cities before he returns home. Naturally he is interested in doing this in as short a time as possible, or perhaps he may be concerned about doing it as cheaply as possible. One can, of course, always solve the problem by trial and error, finding out the time, distance or cost for the various possible orders of the cities, but for a large number of stops this becomes almost unmanageable. Nevertheless, some large-scale examples have been computed, among them the shortest airline distance for a circuit around all the capital cities in the United States.

Problem Set 2.5

1. Do the graphs in Figure 1.1.1 and Figure 1.1.2 have Hamilton lines?

2. A salesman lives in the city A_1 and is supposed to visit the cities A_2, A_3, A_4. The distances between these cities are

$$A_1A_2 = 120, \qquad A_1A_3 = 140, \qquad A_1A_4 = 180$$

$$A_2A_3 = 70, \qquad A_2A_4 = 100, \qquad A_3A_4 = 110.$$

Find the shortest round trip from A_1 through the other three cities.

2.6 Puzzles and Graphs

Previously we discussed how one could find the way from one place to another in a graph. This problem may be considered to be a sort of game, and in spite of the fact that it appears to be quite a simple-minded pastime it actually represents the main content of many puzzles and solitary games.

Let us use the very ancient *Ferryman's Puzzle* to illustrate what we have in mind. A ferryman (f) has been charged with bringing across a river a dog (d), a sheep (s), and a bag of cabbage (c). His little rowboat can only carry one of the items at a time; furthermore, he cannot leave the dog alone with the sheep, nor the sheep with the cabbage. How shall he proceed?

We analyze the various possible alternatives. The only permissible first move is to bring the sheep over; this changes the group at the starting point from f, d, s, c to d, c. He then comes back alone, making it f, d, c. Next he can take either d or c across, leaving c or d. In either case he must take s back, giving f, s, d or f, s, c at the starting point, as the case may be. On his next trip he takes d (or c) across, leaving only s. Finally he comes back alone and transports s across.

Thus in this extremely simple case one has only the permissible moves which have been indicated in the graph in Figure 2.6.1. This shows that the solution can be reached in two ways, each by an arc from the initial position f, d, s, c to the final position "none".

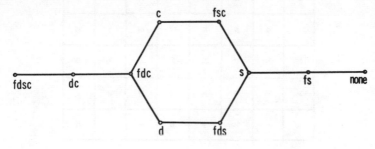

Figure 2.6.1

A problem of a quite similar type is the *Puzzle of the Three Jealous Husbands*: Three married couples on a journey come to a river where they find a little skiff which cannot take more than two persons at a time. The crossing is complicated by the fact that the husbands are all very jealous and will not permit their wives to be left without them in a company where there are other men present.

We shall leave it to the reader to draw the graph of the permissible moves and show how the transfer can be effected.

As we have seen in the preceding examples one can conceive of a graph as a game. The vertices are the various positions in the game and the edges represent the moves which are permitted according to the rules. A usual problem is to decide whether or not one can move from one given position to another stepwise, along edges of the graph. In the language of graph theory this becomes the question: Are the two positions in the same connected component of the graph?

As a further simple example let us consider for a moment a game consisting in moving the knight of a chess game around the board according to the usual rule. Since there are 64 squares on the board the corresponding graph has 64 vertices. It is not difficult to see that the knight can reach any square from any original position so the game graph is connected.

63	22	15	40	1	42	59	18
14	39	64	21	60	17	2	43
37	62	23	16	41	4	19	58
24	13	38	61	20	57	44	3
11	36	25	52	29	46	5	56
26	51	12	33	8	55	30	45
35	10	49	28	53	32	47	6
50	27	34	9	48	7	54	31

Figure 2.6.2

In some of the earliest manuscripts on chess one runs across the following question: Is it possible to move the knight from some arbitrary starting position around the whole board and return it to the starting point so that each square has been occupied just once? This as one sees is the same as finding a Hamilton line for the graph. There are in fact many solutions; one of them is given in Figure 2.6.2.

There is a large number of different moves the knight may make from one square to another. One may ask whether it is possible to find a cyclic path which includes them all just once. This corresponds to the construction of an Euler line in the graph and so, according to our general result, we must examine whether the local degrees are all even. In Figure 2.6.3 we have indicated for each square how many possible knight's moves there are, that is, the local degrees of the vertices of the graph. There are, as one sees, 8 squares with the odd degree 3, so the graph has no Euler line.

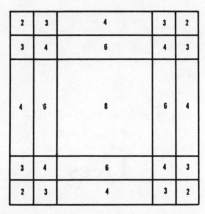

Figure 2.6.3

Problem Set 2.6

1. Prove that the puzzle of the jealous husbands cannot be solved for 4 couples.

2. Prove that it can be solved for 4 couples if the ferryboat holds 3 persons.

3. How many moves of the knight are there on the chess board?

4. Solve the corresponding problems for the moves of the king.

5. Verify that the numbers in each row and the numbers in each column in Figure 2.6.2 give the same sum, 260.

CHAPTER THREE

Trees

3.1 Trees and Forests

A *tree* is a connected graph that has no circuits. This means in particular that there are no multiple edges. It also implies that in a tree there is a unique arc connecting any pair of vertices. Graphs without circuits have connected components which are trees; this makes it natural to extend the botanical terminology and call such graphs *forests*.

To construct a tree one selects some particular vertex A_0. From A_0 one draws edges to neighboring vertices $A_1, A_2, \cdots$; from these one draws edges to their neighbors $A_{11}, A_{12}, \cdots, A_{21}, A_{22}, \cdots$ and so on as indicated in Figure 3.1.1. The particular vertex A_0 which we have chosen in Figure 3.1.1 is called the *root* of the tree; any vertex could have been used as root.

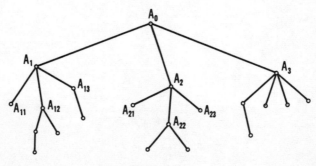

Figure 3.1.1

34

Since there are no circuits in the tree the various arcs (or branches) from A_0 must remain apart once they have become separated, just like the branches of an ordinary tree. Each branch in the graph must have a last *terminal edge* to a *terminal vertex* from which there are no further edges.

According to this observation one can also construct the tree by successively hanging on edges at the vertices. This makes it possible to tell how many edges there are in a tree. The simplest tree is a single edge; it has two vertices and one edge. Each time an edge is added at the end of a branch one also adds a vertex so that we can conclude:

THEOREM 3.1. *A tree with n vertices has n — 1 edges.*

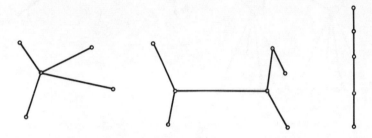

Figure 3.1.2

Instead of taking a tree one could have considered a forest with k connected components, all trees (Figure 3.1.2). In each component tree there is one edge fewer than the number of vertices so that we may state:

THEOREM 3.2. *A forest with k components and n vertices has n — k edges.*

There are many applications of trees. At this stage let us mention only that any sorting process can be pictured in the form of a tree. For instance, one may consider Figure 3.1.1 to be the image of a mail sorting. An original bunch of letters is placed at A_0. The domestic mail may be sorted to A_1, the mail for Europe to A_2, the mail to the Far East to A_3, and so on. The domestic mail at A_1 is sorted next into Eastern, Western, Central mail; the European mail at A_2 may be sorted according to countries, and so on.

The process of sorting punch cards may be represented by a graph in the same way, only here the tree usually would take on a quite regular shape. This is due to the fact that the locations of the punch holes on a card are arranged in regular columns, mostly with 10 punch places in each column. Therefore, when one sorts according to the holes in the first column there are 10 alternatives, A_0, A_1, A_2, $\cdots$, A_9; at each of these there will again be 10 alternatives, e.g. A_{00}, A_{01}, $\cdots$, A_{09}, and so on (see Figure 3.1.3). In reality, the whole procedure can be considered to be a sorting of numbers according to the first, second, etc., digit. Indeed, it is possible to conceive of any tree as a kind of very general number system.

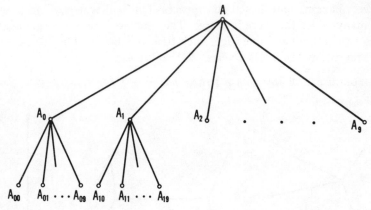

Figure 3.1.3

3.2 Circuits and Trees

Let us formulate our next problem in agricultural terms. In Figure 3.2.1 we have drawn a map of farm fields. We shall think of this map as representing a number of rice fields on an island; the fields are surrounded by earthen dams and these, in turn, are surrounded by the waters of a lake.

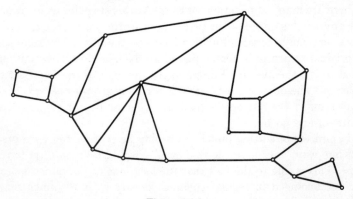

Figure 3.2.1

As is usual in rice cultivation, we want to set the fields under water by opening up some of the walls. In order to immerse every field one must evidently break at least one wall in each circuit in the map, that is, the remaining unbroken walls must give us a graph without circuits. The question is then: How many walls is it necessary to pierce?

This brings us to a general problem concerning graphs: In a connected graph, what is the smallest number of edges that must be removed in order that no circuits remain?

Suppose that we first eliminate an edge $\mathcal{E} = (A, B)$ belonging to some circuit in the graph. Then the graph remains connected, because instead of passing from A to B on $\mathcal{E}$, we can proceed from A to B on the remaining part of the circuit. If after $\mathcal{E}$ has been removed there are further circuits, we eliminate another edge in the same way. By continuing in this manner we must finally come to a connected graph without circuits, that is, a tree $\mathcal{T}$.

When we have arrived at this stage it is simple to determine the number of edges which have been removed. The tree $\mathcal{T}$ has the same number n of vertices as the original graph G. According to Theorem 3.1 there are $n - 1$ edges in $\mathcal{T}$. Therefore, if G originally had N edges we have removed exactly

$$\gamma = N - n + 1$$

edges. This number we call the *circuit rank* of the graph G; other names are also in use, for instance, the *cyclomatic number*. It is the difference of the number of edges and the number of vertices of G increased by 1.

We have established that, in order to reduce a graph G to a tree, one must always remove at least γ edges. In order to reduce G to a forest consisting of several trees, one must always remove more than γ edges, since (according to Theorem 3.2) a forest of n vertices has fewer edges than a tree of n vertices.

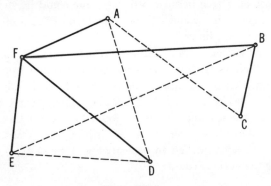

Figure 3.2.2

Let us illustrate the reduction on the graph in Figure 1.1.2. Here the edge ED belongs to the circuit EFD and we remove it first. The edge AD belongs to the circuit DFA and is removed. Finally AC and BE are eliminated. This leaves us with the tree in Figure 3.2.2. Here we have removed

$$\gamma = 4 = 9 - 6 + 1$$

edges.

Problem Set 3.2

1. Verify the results on the graphs in Figure 1.1.2 and Figure 3.2.1.

2. What is the circuit rank for a complete graph?

3.3   The Connector Problem

We turn to a communication problem that has some very practical uses and pose it first in the form of a road construction question. We have a certain number of cities $A, B, C, \cdots$ and we want to construct a road or railroad net connecting all of them. For any pair of cities A, B we know the cost $c(A, B)$ of constructing a connecting line between them. The problem is to build the whole network as cheaply as possible. Instead of using railroads, one can illustrate the situation by means of electrical wire connections or water mains or gas and oil pipes.

In the special case where there are only three cities A, B and C it will be sufficient to build one of the connecting lines

$$ABC, \quad ACB, \quad BAC.$$

If BC is the most expensive stretch then it should be left out and the connecting links BAC should be built.

We turn next to the general case. The graph of the cheapest connecting network must be a tree because otherwise one could leave out a link in a circuit and the cities would still be connected. Thus if one has n cities there must be $n - 1$ links.

We shall show that a minimal cost network can be constructed according to the following simple *economy rule*: In the first step one connects the two cities with the cheapest connecting link $\mathcal{E}_1$. In each step thereafter one adds the cheapest possible link $\mathcal{E}_i$ producing a tree together with the edges already selected; if there should be several links having the same cost, it does not matter which one is used. Any tree $\mathcal{T}$ constructed in this manner may be called an *economy tree*. Its cost $c(\mathcal{T})$ is the sum of the costs for the various edges;

$$c(\mathcal{T}) = c(\mathcal{E}_1) + c(\mathcal{E}_2) + \cdots + c(\mathcal{E}_{n-1}).$$

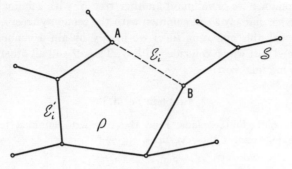

Figure 3.3.1

There remains the essential point: to demonstrate that no other connecting tree S can have a lower cost $c(S)$ than an economy tree. Take S to be a connecting tree with the smallest cost and T any economy tree. Suppose the edges $\mathcal{E}_1, \mathcal{E}_2, \cdots$ of the economy tree T are numbered in the order in which they were added in the construction of T. If the minimal cost tree S is not identical with T, then T has at least one edge not in S; let $\mathcal{E}_i = (A, B)$ be the first edge of T not in S, and let $P(A, B)$ be the path in S connecting the vertices A and B. If the edge $\mathcal{E}_i$ is added to S, the graph $S + \mathcal{E}_i$ will have a circuit $C = \mathcal{E}_i + P(A, B)$ and since T has no circuit, C must contain at least one edge, say $\mathcal{E}'_i$, not in T. We remove this edge and obtain the tree

$$S' = S + \mathcal{E}_i - \mathcal{E}'_i$$

with the same vertices as S and whose cost is

$$c(S') = c(S) + c(\mathcal{E}_i) - c(\mathcal{E}'_i).$$

Since S has the smallest possible cost,

$$c(\mathcal{E}_i) \geq c(\mathcal{E}'_i).$$

But $\mathcal{E}_i$ was the link with the smallest cost such that when added to $\mathcal{E}_1, \mathcal{E}_2, \cdots, \mathcal{E}_{i-1}$ no circuit was produced. Since $\mathcal{E}'_i$ when added to these edges does not give any circuit we conclude that

$$c(\mathcal{E}_i) = c(\mathcal{E}'_i)$$

and so also S' has minimal cost

$$c(S) = c(S').$$

In this manner we have found another tree $\mathcal{S}'$ with minimal cost and one more edge, namely $\mathcal{E}_i$, in common with the economy tree $\mathcal{T}$. But then we can repeat this operation until we finally obtain a connecting tree with minimal cost which coincides with $\mathcal{T}$. Thus $\mathcal{T}$ and all other economy trees have minimal cost.

Problem Set 3.3

1. Draw 6 points in the plane. Find the tree with minimal total length whose edges connect these vertices.

3.4 Streets and Squares

Changing the names of streets and public squares has been a favorite pastime for city councils all over the world—in some places more than in others. Suppose now that the city fathers want to be very systematic about their street names. Each street shall be a block long and each street shall carry the same name as one of its adjoining street intersections; so for instance Washington Avenue or Street shall have one of its ends at Washington Square.

We, naturally, want to put the question in a general graph form. A connected graph is given. When is it possible to let each edge correspond in a unique manner to one of its end vertices?

We point out to begin with that this is always the case when the graph is a tree. After we have selected an arbitrary root A_0 in the tree as in Figure 3.1.1 we let the edge A_0A_1 correspond to the vertex A_1, similarly A_0B_1 to B_1 and A_0C_1 to C_1. In the next step A_1A_2 corresponds to A_2, and so on; in general, any edge $A_{i-1}A_i$ corresponds to the vertex A_i which is farthest away from A_0.

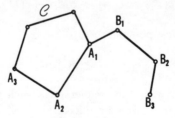

Figure 3.4.1

Suppose next that the graph has a circuit $\mathcal{C}$ (Figure 3.4.1). Each edge in $\mathcal{C}$ shall correspond to one of its end vertices, that is, to a vertex on $\mathcal{C}$. If for instance the edge A_1A_2 corresponds to A_2 then the edge A_2A_3 must correspond to A_3, and so on. No edge not in $\mathcal{C}$ can correspond to a vertex on $\mathcal{C}$.

As a consequence any edge A_1B_1 touching $\mathcal{C}$ at A_1 must correspond to B_1 and any edge B_1B_2 to B_2 and so on. But such an arc $A_1B_1B_2B_3 \cdots$ cannot return to $\mathcal{C}$ because these vertices have already been matched with edges of the circuit. Nor can the arc run back into itself for the same reason.

We see therefore that the part of the graph which one can reach from A_1 beginning in edges A_1B_1 touching $\mathcal{C}$ must be a tree $\mathcal{T}_1$ with the root A_1 and similarly for every other vertex A_i on $\mathcal{C}$. But we just noted that in a tree $\mathcal{T}_1$ one can let each edge correspond to that endpoint which is farthest away from the root A_1. Since the edges on $\mathcal{C}$ correspond to the A_i we have obtained as a result of this analysis:

In a connected graph one can let each edge correspond uniquely to one of its end vertices if and only if the graph is a tree or it consists of a single circuit $\mathcal{C}$ with trees growing at its vertices. (See Figure 3.4.2.) According to Theorem 2.1 a tree has one more vertex than it has edges; a circuit, or a circuit with trees growing from its vertices has the same number of edges and vertices. Thus the possibility of matching edges with vertices is to be expected in these cases.

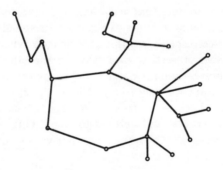

Figure 3.4.2

A tree as in Figure 3.1.1, or a graph as in Figure 3.4.2, can represent a street map only for very small towns where there are no real city blocks, or where there is only one central block to which the roads lead in from the country.

After reflecting a little upon the situation the city council members proudly become aware of the fact that their town is much too large for the use of this method. Instead they agree to substitute the following principle: The streets and the squares shall be so named that at each square there is a street with the same name, that is, for instance, at Washington Square there must always be a Washington Street running into it.

In terms of graph theory this means matching each vertex to a unique adjoining edge. There are cases in which this cannot be done; a tree, for example, has one more vertex than it has edges, as we saw in Theorem 3.1. But here it can almost be done. Let us look at the illustration of a tree in Figure 3.1.1. One can associate with each vertex that edge which leads from it to the root A_0. This matches each vertex to an edge as desired except for the root itself.

The trees are exceptions in this respect for we have the general result:

In a connected graph which is not a tree one can always match the vertices to adjoining edges.

PROOF. A graph connecting a set of n vertices has at least $n - 1$ edges; if it is not a tree it has more than $n - 1$ edges and can be reduced to a tree by having some edges removed; see Section 3.2. Let $\mathcal{E}_0 = (A_0, B_0)$ be one of the edges removed when the graph is reduced to a tree $\mathcal{T}$, and select A_0 as its root. In $\mathcal{T}$, every vertex except A_0 can be made to correspond to an adjoining edge; the extra edge $\mathcal{E}_0$ of our graph can be assigned to A_0, and now every vertex of the graph is matched with an adjoining edge.

It is of interest to note that according to the preceding discussion one can always either let all vertices of a graph correspond to adjoining edges or let the edges correspond to adjoining vertices. When can one do both? When the number of vertices of a graph is the same as the number of edges. Such a graph cannot be a tree and so we conclude that the graph must have the form we indicated in Figure 3.4.2, having only a single circuit $\mathcal{C}$. Here there is actually a correspondence which works both ways, edges to vertices, and vertices to edges. One lets the edges on $\mathcal{C}$ correspond to vertices on $\mathcal{C}$, while any other vertex not on $\mathcal{C}$ corresponds to the one of its edges nearest to $\mathcal{C}$.

Problem Set 3.4

1. Give a correspondence of vertices to adjoining edges in the graphs in Figure 1.1.1 and Figure 1.1.2.

CHAPTER FOUR

Matchings

4.1 The Jobs and the Applicants

A firm has a number of vacant jobs of various types and also a group
of applicants to fill them. Each man is qualified for certain of the jobs
and so the question comes up: Is it possible to assign each man to a position for which he is suited?

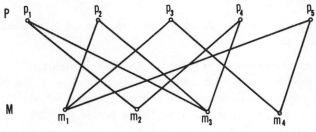

Figure 4.1.1

We can again illustrate the situation by means of a graph, this time
of a somewhat special type. As we have just explained, there is a group
of available men which we shall denote by M, and a set of positions P.
We construct our graph by drawing edges (m, p) connecting each man
m in M with the positions p in P for which he is qualified. Thus there
are no edges connecting two vertices corresponding to the men, nor are
there any edges connecting two jobs. Therefore, the graph has the form
which we have indicated in Figure 4.1.1. A graph of this kind where the

43

set of vertices is decomposed into two separate parts M and P such that there are edges only between M and P is called a *bipartite graph* (Figure 4.1.1).

It is clear that one cannot always expect to have a suitable job for each man. For one thing, there must be at least as many jobs as there are men. But this is not enough. Imagine, for example, that the applicants consist of two carpenters and a man who can do both woodwork and plumbing, and that there are four job openings for these three men, one in carpentry and three in plumbing. Then, clearly, one of the carpenters will remain jobless although there are more jobs than applicants, and although our three men, collectively, qualify for both available trades.

Suppose there are altogether N men applying for positions. Then in order to be able to solve our assignment problem the following condition will have to be fulfilled:

If one takes out any group of k men, for all $k = 1, 2, \cdots, N$, then there must be at least k jobs for which, collectively, they are qualified.

For example, of one man were a carpenter and the other a carpenter who can also do plumbing and if two plumbing jobs were available, then this condition would be violated for $k = 1$, although it holds for $k = 2$, and the men could not be placed.

We shall call the italicized statement the *diversity condition* for short. Our principal purpose now is to show that the condition is actually sufficient, that is, to prove

THEOREM 4.1. *One can always assign a suitable job to each man when the diversity condition is fulfilled.*

The result is not simple to prove. It is simple enough for $N = 1$: if a man is qualified for a job he can be put into it. If $N = 2$, the diversity condition guarantees that there are at least two jobs for which the two men are qualified, and that, moreover, the carpenter–plumber catastrophe does not occur, i.e., that each man is qualified for at least one job. Once again the men can be placed.

These remarks show that the theorem is true for $N = 1$ and for $N = 2$. It is reasonable to try to prove the theorem in general by the principle of mathematical induction: we shall assume that the statement is true when there are $N - 1$ men or fewer and we shall deduce that it is true when there are N men.

If the diversity condition holds, it may hold with room to spare, or just barely. It may, that is, happen that every possible group of k men ($k = 1, 2, \cdots, N - 1$) qualifies for more than k jobs (room to spare), or it may happen that for some k_0 ($k_0 = 1, \cdots, N - 1$) there is a group of k_0 men who qualify for exactly k_0 jobs (just barely). We shall prove that in either case we can always assign a suitable job to each of the N men.

If the diversity condition holds with room to spare, pick any one of the N men and place him in one of the jobs for which he is suited. Among the remaining $N - 1$ men no group of k (for any k) can be qualified for fewer than k jobs, because among the originally available jobs there were at least $k + 1$ these men were suited for, and the assignment already made took at most one job opportunity away from them. By the induction assumption, the $N - 1$ men can be put into suitable jobs.

If the diversity condition holds just barely, consider some set A_0 of k_0 men ($k_0 < N$) who are qualified for just k_0 jobs. Because of the diversity condition, no k of these men (for $k = 1, 2, \cdots, k_0$) can be qualified for fewer than k jobs; it follows from the induction assumption that the k_0 men in A_0 can be placed. It remains to consider the $N - k_0$ men who are left. We must prove that the diversity condition is still satisfied for them and for the unfilled jobs, i.e., that for any group B of k of these men ($k = 1, 2, \cdots, N - k_0$) there are still at least k unfilled jobs. To see this, suppose that the men in group B qualify for only k' jobs, where k' is less than k. Then the set $A_0 + B$ consisting of the $k_0 + k$ men in A_0 and in B would originally have been qualified for only $k_0 + k'$ jobs; this is contrary to the assumed validity of the diversity condition. We conclude that the diversity condition holds for the remaining $N - k_0$ men, who can therefore be placed in suitable jobs by the induction assumption; this completes the proof of the theorem.

Figure 4.1.2 shows the case $N = 6$. The first three vertices on the lower line represent a group A_0 of $k_0 = 3$ men qualified, respectively, for plumbing (p), carpentry and plumbing (cp), and carpentry (c), and the edges lead to positions (vertices on the upper line) filled by these men. The remaining three vertices represent $N - k_0 = 3$ men qualified, respectively, for bricklaying (b), plumbing (p), and toolmaking (t). We observe that the diversity condition is violated for a group B of $k = 2$ of these men, the bricklayer and the plumber; there is no plumbing job among the unfilled positions, and only one bricklaying job. Clearly, the diversity condition is therefore also violated for the set $A_0 + B$ of five men because there were to begin with only four positions for which they qualified.

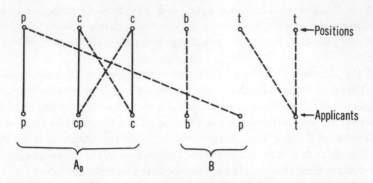

Figure 4.1.2

4.2   Other Formulations

When we introduced a bipartite graph, as for instance in Figure 4.1.1, we considered the one set M of vertices to be the applicants and the other set P as the available positions. Assume now that one can assign a suitable job to each man. This means in terms of the graph that one can find one edge at each vertex in M such that each of these edges goes to a different vertex in P. Therefore, one often says that one has a graph matching of the vertices in M into the vertices in P (Figure 4.2.1).

We saw that such a matching of M into P was possible if and only if the diversity condition was fulfilled, that is, any k vertices in M were connected by edges to at least k vertices in P. If P and M have the same number of vertices then such a matching gives a one-to-one correspondence between the vertices in M and P such that corresponding vertices in the matching are connected by a graph edge (Figure 4.2.2).

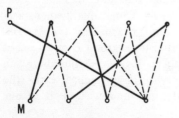

Figure 4.2.1

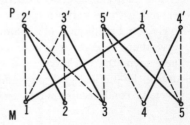

Figure 4.2.2

This problem of finding graph matchings has been formulated in many ways. Sometimes it is called the *Marriage Problem*: Suppose that we have a group of boys and a group of girls, each with the same number of individuals. Some of them know each other already and the question is: When is it possible to pair the two groups in such a manner that the boy and the girl in a pair in each case are already acquainted with each other?

One can also put the problem in reverse and state it as follows: In a small village there is the same number of boys and girls of marriageable age. By taboos and custom the boys are not permitted to marry close relatives: sisters, half-sisters or cousins. When is it possible for all the boys to take a bride within the village? As before we can depict the possibilities for marriage for each individual by means of a bipartite graph, only in this case they should be connected by an edge when they are not related.

Let us give another twist to our problem. In your class in school there will be a certain number of committees; we may name them

$$C: \quad C_1, C_2, \cdots, C_N.$$

Naturally each of these N committees must have a chairman. In order to avoid too dominating an influence by a small group, it has been stipulated that no member shall be permitted to be chairman of more than one committee. Again we have the question: Under what conditions is this possible? It is not always possible; when there are too many committees in a relatively small class we may be in trouble with this rule.

To solve the problem we turn to the bipartite graphs as before. In this case one of the vertex sets C in the graph shall consist of the N committees, the other vertex set P consists of the pupils in the class. We draw an edge from a committee C_i to a pupil p only if p is a member of C_i. In this case the diversity condition runs as follows: Any group of k committees $(k = 1, 2, \cdots, N)$ shall include at least k distinct pupils. According to our theorem this is the condition that it be possible to select separate chairmen.

After we have put our problem in this form we have in reality deduced a theorem which was published by the English mathematician Philip Hall in 1935: A number N of sets C are given; each has members p from a set P. We wish to assign to each set C_i one of its members p_i such that different sets have been assigned a different element in P. This is possible only if the following condition is fulfilled: Any k sets C_i $(k = 1, 2, \cdots, N)$ shall include at least k different elements of P.

Let us return once more to the committee formulation of our problem. If there is a fairly large number of committees it is not always easy to verify that the diversity condition is satisfied. One may ask, therefore, whether it might be possible to give some simple rule for the selection of the committees insuring that distinct chairmen can always be found.

This is actually feasible. To illustrate what we have in mind suppose that every committee has at least 5 members. Then in the graph there are at least 5 edges from each vertex in C. From a group of k committees there would be at least $5k$ edges to vertices in P. (See Figure 4.2.3 for $k = 4$.) Now if we restrict the number of committees to which any pupil can belong to at most 5, this means that the edges from the k committees must go to at least k individuals in P, hence the diversity condition is fulfilled.

This argument is quite general and so we may formulate the result:

Let it be stipulated that each committee have at least t members; furthermore, no individual is permitted to belong to more than t committees. Then it is always possible to find a separate chairman for each committee.

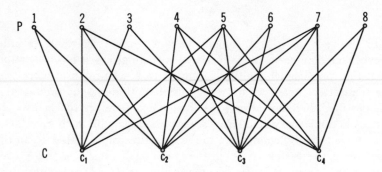

Figure 4.2.3

Problem Set 4.2

1. Give an example of a set of committees which cannot have separate chairmen.

2. How many committees of three members can one form in a class of 12 pupils? Would it be possible to assign separate chairmen to each of them?

3. Find a matching in Figure 4.1.1.

4.3 Round-Robin Matchings

In all tournaments one is faced with the question of how the individual participants should be paired as the match progresses. In the case of a knock-out tournament the problem is simple: all losers drop out in each round and one pairs the remaining winners, possibly letting one man have a bye if there is an odd number of players left.

The problem is somewhat more complicated in the case of a Round-Robin tournament, one of the usual kinds of chess tournament. Here every player must play against every other player and one wishes to prepare a tournament schedule in advance, giving the pairs of opponents in each round.

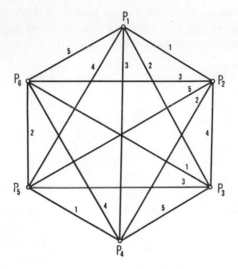

Figure 4.3.1

This situation can again be interpreted conveniently in graph terms. We suppose that there are N players so that each of them plays $N - 1$ games with the other participants. A game is represented as before as an edge (A, B) connecting two players or vertices A and B. The totality of games then corresponds to the complete graph on N vertices. In Figure 4.3.1 the situation is presented for $N = 6$.

A round in the tournament consists in matching the players in pairs; for the moment we suppose that N is an even number so that this may be done. In the graph the matching corresponds to a selection of $\frac{1}{2}N$ non-adjoining edges, one at each of the N vertices. In the next round one must select an entirely different set of $\frac{1}{2}N$ edges, and so on, until all games have been played. In Figure 4.3.1 the edges have been marked in this way: those carrying the number 1 belong to matchings in the first round, those with the number 2 to the second round, and so on.

If there is a large number of players the actual production of a schedule for the matchings in the various rounds becomes quite laborious unless there is some systematic method for doing it. Most handbooks on tournament management include extensive tables of matchings for various numbers of players, $N = 6, 8, 10, 12$, etc. For the arrangement of the schedules it is sufficient to suppose, as above, that the number of players N is even so that they may be paired; if there should be an odd number of players one can always add a fictitious player F and then stipulate that anyone who is matched with F has a bye in that particular round.

	1	2	3	4	5	6	·	·	·	·	N
2		~~2~~1	N	N − 1	N − 2	N − 3	·	·	·	4	3
3		4	~~3~~1	2	N	N − 1	·	·	·	6	5
4		6	5	~~4~~1	3	2	N	·	·	8	7
·		·	·	·	·	·	·	·	·	·	·
·		·	·	·	·	·	·	·	·	·	·
·		·	·	·	·	·	·	·	·	·	·
$\frac{1}{2}N + 1$		N	N − 1	N − 2	·		·		·	3	2
$\frac{1}{2}N + 2$		3	2	N	N − 1	·		·	·	5	4
·		·	·	·	·	·	·	·	·	·	·
·		·	·	·	·	·	·	·	·	·	·
·		·	·	·	·	·	·	·	·	·	·
N		N − 1	N − 2	·		·		·	·	2	~~N~~1

Figure 4.3.2

Let us describe a simple and general method for the construction of a tournament schedule for an even number of players N. We number the players 1, 2, $\cdots$, N and write these figures, in this order, in the first line of a square array. We want the next line in the array to feature the opponents of the players named in the first line during the first round of the match. Similarly, on the line below that, we want to name the opponents of players 1, 2, 3, $\cdots$, N in the second round and so on, until all players have played each other. Clearly, our scheme should be such that all possible pairs of players encounter each other exactly once. One way of achieving this is shown in the table below. To identify the opponent of player j in the kth round, just look in the column under j, k lines below, in the array shown in Figure 4.3.2.

This table is made as follows:

The first row, as already observed, enumerates the players from 1 to N; we also fill these numbers into the first column (see Figure 4.3.2). Now into the remaining $N - 1$ places in each row we enter the numbers from 2 to N in cyclic descending order. The first $\frac{1}{2}N$ lines begin with the even numbers 2, 4, $\cdots$, N and read

$$
\begin{array}{cccccccc}
2, & N, & N-1, & \cdot & \cdot & \cdot\ \cdot\ \cdot & 4, & 3, \\
4, & 3, & 2, & N, & N-1, & \cdot\ \cdot\ \cdot & 6, & 5, \\
\cdot & \cdot & \cdot & \cdot & \cdot & \cdot\ \cdot\ \cdot\ \cdot & & \\
\cdot & \cdot & \cdot & \cdot & \cdot & \cdot\ \cdot\ \cdot\ \cdot & & \\
N, & N-1, & N-2, & \cdot & \cdot & \cdot\ \cdot\ \cdot & 3, & 2;
\end{array}
$$

the next $N - 1$ lines begin with the odd numbers 3, 5, $\cdots$, $N - 1$ and read

$$
\begin{array}{cccccccc}
3 & 2 & N & N-1 & \cdot & \cdot & 5, & 4, \\
5 & 4 & 3 & 2 & N & N-1 \cdot\ \cdot & 7, & 6, \\
\cdot & \cdot & \cdot & \cdot & \cdot & \cdot & \cdot & \cdot \\
\cdot & \cdot & \cdot & \cdot & \cdot & \cdot & \cdot & \cdot \\
N-1 & N-2 & \cdot & \cdot & \cdot & \cdot & 2 & N.
\end{array}
$$

Observe that we have failed to enter the number 1 in this table; on the other hand, since a player does not play against himself, the number at the head of any column should never be repeated within that column. Both matters are taken care of if we replace all numbers occurring in the main diagonal by 1's as indicated. Now each player finds under his number the player he is to have as opponent in the various rounds—for instance, the player having the number 4 plays with $N - 1$ in the first round, with 2 in the second round, with 1 in the third round, 6 in the fourth round, and so on, until he finally plays with $N - 3$ in the $(N - 1)$st round.

Problem Set 4.3

1. Construct tournament tables for $N = 6, 8, 10$.

2. To prove that the preceding table is actually a usable schedule we must verify the following facts:

   a) Every player has one game with every other player in the tournament.

   b) Each player has a different opponent in each round.

   c) When the player j plays the player k in a round then the table must also give j as the player opposing k.

CHAPTER FIVE

Directed Graphs

5.1 Team Competitions Re-examined

In the first chapter we used team competitions as a way of introducing graphs (Section 1.1). We joined two teams, say A and C, by an edge (A, C) in the corresponding graph whenever these two teams had played together (see Figure 1.1.1). But when the various games played have been represented in this manner there is one essential fact missing: Who won the game?

This deficiency can readily be remedied. Usually one draws an arrowhead on the edge (A, C) in question. When this arrowhead points from A to C we let it signify that team A won over team C. Suppose that we have the record of the outcomes of the various games which have been played and add all the corresponding arrowheads in the graph in Figure 1.1.1. It may then appear as depicted in Figure 5.1.1. From this graph one reads off that A won over C but F lost to D, while B won all its games with C, E and F, and so on.

A graph G where a direction is indicated for every edge we call a *directed graph*. It may be intended, as we indicated, to be the image of the results of a competition between teams or individuals; on the other hand, any directed graph can be conceived of as a geometric picture of a competition.

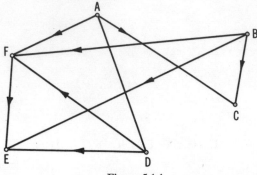

Figure 5.1.1

We have passed over one point in silence: What happens when a game ends in a draw? On the whole draws are a nuisance for the score keeping in any kind of a tournament. Often the rules are so formulated that draws cannot occur, as, for instance, in tennis or squash. In other games, such as golf and soccer, the players and teams play extra rounds to avoid an undecided match. But if draws are unavoidable we may take them into account in the graph by letting the corresponding edges remain undirected. Then we obtain a *mixed graph* in which some edges are directed and others undirected. This type of graph occurs also in other problems as we shall see.

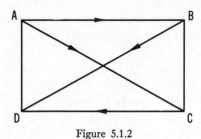

Figure 5.1.2

As an illustration of mixed graphs we may take Figure 5.1.2 in which the four teams A, B, C, and D all have played a game with one another: A has won over B and C and drawn with D; B lost to A, drew with C, and won over D; C lost to A, won over D and drew with B; D drew with A and lost to B and C.

5.2 The Problems of One-Way Traffic

The map of any network of roads or streets furnished us with a somewhat special, yet illustrative example of a graph. But an up-to-date city plan should show not only the relative locations of the streets and their intersections; it should also give information about which streets have a two-way traffic flow and which streets have one-way traffic, together with the direction in the latter case. Clearly, we are again faced with a directed graph, or rather, with a mixed graph if not all streets have one-way directions (Figure 5.2.1). One can make the whole graph directed by a device often used in graph theory, namely by replacing an undirected edge by two directed edges, one in each direction, between the same two vertices.

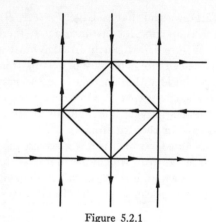

Figure 5.2.1

One-way traffic in a city poses questions which are of interest also for general graphs. Suppose that the police department in a town decides to introduce a new traffic plan so radical that every street is made one-way. This would certainly bring an awful outcry from the citizenry if it were discovered that one could not always drive legally from one place to another. This brings up the problem: When is it possible to direct the streets in such a manner that one can pass from any point to any other along the prescribed directions? In the more general graph formulation the corresponding problem would read: When can the edges of a graph G be given directions in such a way that there is a directed path from any vertex to any other?

It is clear that the graph must be connected. But there are other conditions which must be satisfied. A graph edge $\mathcal{E} = (A, B)$ is called a *separating edge*, or sometimes a *bridge*, when there is no way of getting from A to B or vice versa except through $\mathcal{E}$. A separating edge $\mathcal{E}$ divides the vertices in the graph G into two sets, namely those vertices one can reach from A without traversing $\mathcal{E}$ and those one can reach from B without traversing $\mathcal{E}$. This corresponds to a separation of the graph G into two parts, G_1 and G_2, connected only by the edge $\mathcal{E}$ (Figure 5.2.2).

On a city map a separating edge would be a single connection between two separate parts of town; perhaps it may be a single bridge over a river or a single railroad underpass. Clearly if such a connection were made into a one-way street, no vehicle could leave one part of the town to get to the other.

Earlier (Section 3.1), we said that an edge $\mathcal{E} = (A, B)$ was a *terminal edge* if at one of the endpoints, for instance at A, there were no other edges of the graph (Figure 5.2.3). Such an edge must also be regarded as a separating edge since there is no way of getting from A to B except through $\mathcal{E}$. One may consider that in this case the graph G_1 in Figure 5.2.2 has shrunk to a single vertex A. On a street map a terminal edge corresponds to a dead-end street; it cannot be made one-way without blocking the access to A or the exit from A.

If $\mathcal{E}_1 = (A_1, B_1)$ is an edge which is not a separating edge there must be some other way from A_1 to B_1 which does not pass through $\mathcal{E}_1$ (Figure 5.2.4). For this reason such an edge $\mathcal{E}_1$ is called a *circuit edge*. There are therefore two types of edges in a graph, circuit edges and separating edges.

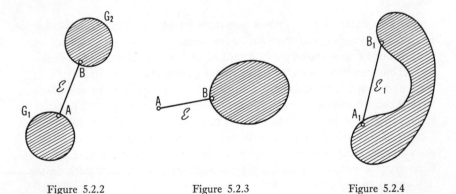

Figure 5.2.2   Figure 5.2.3   Figure 5.2.4

We are now ready to prove the following:

THEOREM 5.1. *If G is an undirected connected graph then one can always direct the circuit edges of G and leave the separating edges undirected so that there is a directed path from any given vertex to any other.*

In terms of a city map this may be expressed as follows: If one leaves the single bridges and dead-end streets as two-way passages, all other streets can be made one-way in such a manner that the traffic is assured satisfactory connections everywhere.

We can prove the theorem by giving a method for directing the graph edges suitably. We begin by taking some arbitrary edge $\mathcal{E} = (A, B)$ in G. If $\mathcal{E}$ is a separating edge it shall remain two-way and so one can get to B from A and vice versa along $\mathcal{E}$ (Figure 5.2.5). On the other hand, if $\mathcal{E}$ is a circuit edge on a circuit $\mathcal{C}$ all edges on $\mathcal{C}$ may be directed in circular fashion; evidently one can always get from one vertex to another on $\mathcal{C}$ by following the edge directions (Figure 5.2.6).

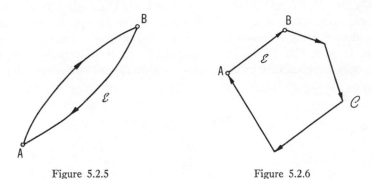

Figure 5.2.5   Figure 5.2.6

We have made a small beginning on directing the graph and this can be steadily enlarged. Suppose that we have directed a certain part H of the graph G in question so that the theorem holds for H. Since G is connected, if H is not the whole graph there must be some edge $\mathcal{E} = (A, B)$ touching H; that is, $\mathcal{E}$ does not belong to H but has one of its end vertices, say A, on H.

If $\mathcal{E}$ is a separating edge we agreed that it must remain two-way. Therefore, from any vertex X in H one can proceed by a directed path $\mathcal{R}$ to A and then through $\mathcal{E}$ to B. Conversely one can go from B through

$\mathcal{E}$ to A and then by some directed path $\mathcal{Q}$ from A to X (Figure 5.2.7). Thus one can add $\mathcal{E}$ to H and have a larger part of G which is properly directed.

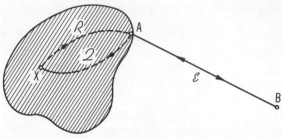

Figure 5.2.7

In the other alternative $\mathcal{E} = (A, B)$ is a circuit edge and so lies on a circuit $\mathcal{C}$. We proceed on $\mathcal{C}$ from A to B and further to the next vertex D of $\mathcal{C}$ which lies on H (Figure 5.2.8). We put a direction on the edges in $\mathcal{C}$ from A to B and further on to D and add these edges to H. Then one can go by a directed path ρ in H from any vertex X in H to the vertex A and then along $\mathcal{C}$ to any vertex Y on $\mathcal{C}$. Conversely, one can proceed from Y along $\mathcal{C}$ to D and by a directed path $\mathcal{Q}$ in H from D to X. By enlarging H repeatedly in this manner one finally gets all edges directed as desired.

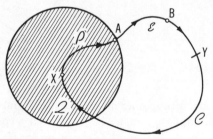

Figure 5.2.8

Creating one-way streets is certainly an effective method of expediting the flow of traffic, but it may also pose real puzzles for a driver unfamiliar with the town who wants to find his way around in a car. In the case of two-way street traffic one can use the procedure outlined in Section 2.4 to pass through every edge of an undirected graph. But this manner of groping around depended for its success essentially upon the fact that one could pass through each edge in both directions. When the streets are one-way, wholly or in part, the situation becomes much more complicated, even when one supposes, as one must, that there is always at least one directed path from any point to any other.

The general problem is: How can one proceed systematically along the given directions of the graph so that one eventually will pass through every edge? The crux of the matter is to have a good memory; better still, one can draw a graph sketch of the streets or edges as one proceeds.

We start at some point a_0 through one of the streets issuing from it. Whenever we pass a street intersection we mark on our sketch which street we came from and which new street we take, and we indicate also the other streets at this corner, together with their directions; these will be explored later. After a while one must return to an intersection a_1 which has been visited before (Figure 5.2.9).

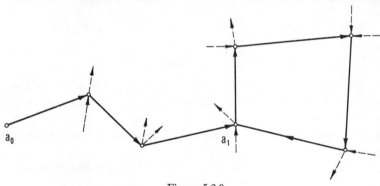

Figure 5.2.9

We look at the part of the map prepared after the departure from a_1 to see which side streets have not been traversed on this section. We select one of them and proceed to it and then through it. By continuing this process we cover more and more streets; many of them will be covered several times, but there will also always be new ones until the whole graph has been traversed. Until this happens we can never be stymied for lack of new streets to pass. Suppose for example that at some stage we were at a vertex a_i and there were still a street (c, d) we had not traversed. By our assumption there is a directed path from a_i to c and this would at some point depart from the paths we had already covered.

Problem Set 5.2

1. Use the preceding method to direct the edges in the graphs in Figure 1.4.2 and Figure 3.2.1.

2. Do the same for the street maps in Figure 5.2.10 and Figure 5.2.11.

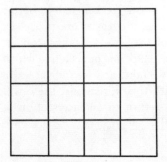   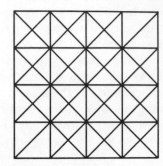

Figure 5.2.10   Figure 5.2.11

5.3 Local Degrees

In Section 1.6 we considered the number of edges of an undirected graph; the local degree $\rho(A)$ at a vertex A was the number of edges having A as one end point. In a directed graph there are two types of edges at each vertex A: the outgoing edges from A and the incoming edges to A. Correspondingly, we have two local degrees—the number $\rho(A)$ of outgoing edges and the number $\rho^*(A)$ of incoming edges. In Figure 5.3.1 we have

$$\rho(A) = 3, \qquad \rho^*(A) = 2$$

Each directed edge $\mathcal{E} = (A, B)$ has one initial vertex A and one terminal vertex B. Therefore one can obtain the total number N of edges either by counting the number of outgoing edges at each vertex or by counting the total number of incoming edges. This means that for a directed graph G with n vertices

$$A_1, \ A_2, \ \cdots, \ A_n$$

the number N of edges is given by either one of the expressions

$$N = \rho(A_1) + \cdots + \rho(A_n) = \rho^*(A_1) + \cdots + \rho^*(A_n).$$

As an example we may take the graph in Figure 5.1.1. Here

$$\rho(B) = \rho(D) = 3, \quad \rho(A) = 2, \quad \rho(F) = 1, \quad \rho(C) = \rho(E) = 0$$

while

$$\rho^*(E) = \rho^*(F) = 3, \quad \rho^*(C) = 2, \quad \rho^*(A) = 1, \quad \rho^*(B) = \rho^*(D) = 0,$$

and in either case the total is 9.

There are various types of directed graphs in which the local degrees have special properties. Let us mention a few. A graph is called *regular of degree r* if all local degrees have the same value r:

$$\rho(A) = \rho^*(A) = r$$

for each vertex A. A simple example is a circuit (Figure 5.3.2); here

$$\rho(A) = \rho^*(A) = 1$$

for every vertex A so that the graph is regular of degree 1.

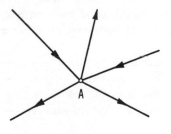

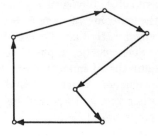

Figure 5.3.1   Figure 5.3.2

As another example let us take the graph of a round-robin tournament in which each team is scheduled to play with every other. Suppose first that there is an even number of competing teams so that there are no byes. Then after k rounds each team will have played k others. In the corresponding graph there must therefore be a total of k edges at each vertex, some incoming, denoting losses, the others outgoing, denoting victories (excluding the possibility of draws). Consequently, the local degrees of our graph must satisfy the conditions

(5.3.1) $$\rho(A) + \rho^*(A) = k$$

at each vertex A.

If the number of teams is odd, then in each round there will be one team that does not play. For the teams which have played in every round the relation (5.3.1) remains satisfied, while for the k teams B which have had a bye it becomes

(5.3.2) $$\rho(B) + \rho^*(B) = k - 1.$$

Problem Set 5.3

1. Draw the graphs of some tournament of 5 teams after 2 and 3 rounds.

2. How must the relations (5.3.1) and (5.3.2) be modified when draws may occur?

3. Draw regular, directed graphs of degree $r = 2$ for $n = 5, 6, 7, 8$ vertices.

5.4 Genetic Graphs

When you draw your family tree you may make use of a directed graph to illustrate the family relationships. A directed edge (A, B) is drawn from a member A to another member B to indicate that B is a child of A. Biologists use this kind of a diagram systematically to describe the outcome of genetic breeding experiments, denoting by a directed edge (A, B) that B is the offspring of A.

Such genetic graphs have some very special properties which come to light almost immediately. One of them is the consequence of sexual reproduction. Since each individual has two parents, one male and the other female, there will be just two incoming edges to each vertex; in our technical terms,

(5.4.1) $$\rho^*(B) = 2.$$

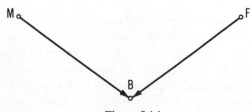

Figure 5.4.1

Thus the basic figure in a genetic graph consists of two edges as in Figure 5.4.1, where B is the offspring of two individuals, the male M and the female F.

We may remark at this point that family trees like ordinary trees do not extend into the heavens. Since our knowledge has limits one always reaches a point at which neither parent, or only one parent, is known. Thus one might properly replace the condition (5.4.1) by the inequality

(5.4.2) $$\rho^*(B) \leq 2.$$

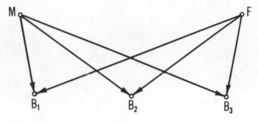

Figure 5.4.2

Any family relationship is expressed by a configuration in the genetic graph. So for instance Figure 5.4.2 informs us that the individuals B_1, B_2, B_3 are brothers or sisters since they are all the children of the same parents M and F.

Similarly Figure 5.4.3 tells us that B_4 is a half-brother or half-sister of the children B_1, B_2, B_3 since they have the same mother F, but different fathers, M and M_1.

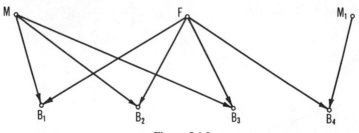

Figure 5.4.3

We now come to a point of interest. Suppose that one has a directed graph of the special type with at most two incoming edges at each vertex, that is, the condition (5.4.2) is satisfied. We may then ask: Is it possible to introduce two sexes in the graph, in other words, to divide the vertices or individuals into two classes, male M and female F, such that the two incoming edges to any vertex always originate one from each group as in Figure 5.4.1?

An example (Figure 5.4.4) shows that this is not always possible. Suppose that we take A_1 to be a male. Since he has a child B_1 with A_2 the latter must be a female. Since A_2 and A_3 have a child B_3, A_3 is also a male. But this contradicts the fact that B_2 is, according to the graph, a child of A_1 and A_3, both males. A similar contradictory situation results if one supposes that A_1 is a female.

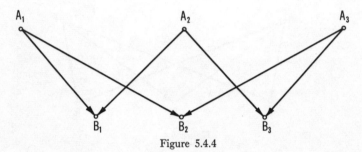

Figure 5.4.4

To analyze the cause of this trouble let us start with some vertex A_1 which we shall call a male. If A_1 has a child B_1 with another parent A_2 then A_2 must be a female. If A_2 also has a child B_2 with another individual A_3, A_3 is a male, and so on. In this manner we obtain an alternating sequence of males and females

$$(5.4.3) \qquad A_1, A_2, \cdots, A_n.$$

In our graph they are connected by a sequence of edges alternately having opposite directions,

$$(A_1, B_1), \quad (A_2, B_1), \quad (A_2, B_2), \quad \cdots, \quad (A_n, B_{n-1}),$$

as indicated in Figure 5.4.5.

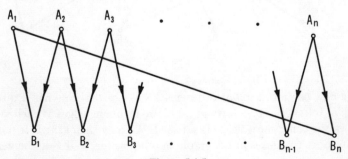

Figure 5.4.5

Suppose now that also A_1 and A_n have a child B_n as in Figure 5.4.5. This results in a *circular alternating path*

(5.4.4) $$(A_1, B_1)(A_2, B_1) \cdots (A_n, B_n)(A_1, B_n)$$

running back into itself. In order that this be compatible with the alternating sex determination in the sequence (5.4.3), the vertices A_1 and A_n must have opposite sex, that is, n must be an even number. This leads to the

Sex condition: Let G be a directed graph in which the condition (5.4.2) *is fulfilled. If a division of the vertices of the graph into two sex groups is possible then each sequence* (5.4.3) *of parents A_i in a circular alternating path must have an even number n of terms.* An equivalent statement of this condition is that, in any circular alternating path (5.4.4), the number of edges is divisible by 4.

If the sex condition is satisfied one can assign a sex to all vertices in the graph. One begins with a vertex A_1 and assigns a sex to it arbitrarily. If A_1 has no children or if these children have no other known parents this ends the sex consequences of A_1. But if A_1 has a child in common with some individual A_2 then one forms all alternating paths from A_1. This determines uniquely the sex of all parents (5.4.3) in the sequences; for if there were an alternating path from A_1 to A_n making A_n a male and another path from A_1 making A_n a female then one could proceed from A_1 to A_n on the first path and return to A_1 on the second. But this would produce a circular alternating path with an odd number of vertices, contrary to the requirement of our sex condition.

In this first step not all vertices will have been given a sex. In the next step we select some vertex A_1' not related to A_1 by an alternating path; to A_1' we assign a sex character arbitrarily and continue as before; then a third vertex A_1'' unrelated to A_1' and A_1 is taken as a starting point, and so on until the whole vertex set has received its characters. From the way in which the sexes have been assigned it follows that one can never run into the contradiction that two males or two females have a child together. It is worth noting in this connection that the sex characters of the vertices in the graph usually can be assigned in many ways.

After we have discovered the condition for a suitable assignment of sexes to the vertices it is natural to ask whether a graph satisfying this condition actually can be realized as the image of a breeding experiment. One finds readily that one further restriction must be imposed on the graph.

Suppose that we have a series of individual organisms

(5.4.5) $$D_1, \quad D_2, \quad \cdots, \quad D_n,$$

each an offspring of the preceding one. In the graph this corresponds to a directed path (Figure 5.4.6). The births of these individuals (5.4.5) must follow in the same order in time. Consequently it cannot happen that D_n becomes the parent of D_1 (Figure 5.4.6), that is, the graph cannot contain any cyclic directed path; such graphs are called *acyclic*.

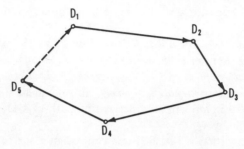

Figure 5.4.6

We have established three necessary conditions for a directed graph to be interpreted as a genetic experiment:

1. $\rho^*(A) \leq 2$ for all A: no vertex has more than two incoming edges.
2. Every circular alternating path has a number of edges divisible by 4.
3. The graph is acyclic.

Conversely, when these conditions are satisfied and sex characters have been suitably assigned, the whole graph may be considered to depict what happens in a genetic experiment; an edge (A_0, B) signifies that B is the offspring of A_0 from a mating with some other (possibly unknown) individual A_1 of the opposite sex.

Our three conditions may therefore be considered to be the rules for a genetic scheme in general. In more everyday language they are the self-evident axioms:

1. Each individual has at most two parents.
2. The parents belong to opposite sexes.
3. No individual is his own ancestor.

To conclude, let us make one further observation about genetic graphs. We have considered our graph to represent the results of an arbitrary genetic experiment in which matings may be induced whenever biologically feasible. In human society the situation is otherwise; well recognized taboos exclude a variety of configurations from our family trees. For instance, since no individual may marry his own sister or brother there can be no configuration in our graph of the form given in Figure 5.4.7. Since no individual may marry one of his parents there are no configurations of the type represented in Figure 5.4.8.

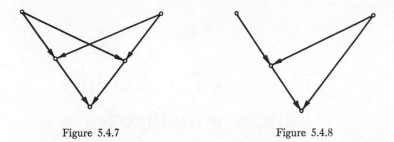

Figure 5.4.7   Figure 5.4.8

Problem Set 5.4

1. Draw the graph which indicates that two individuals are:
   (a) cousins; (b) aunt (or uncle) and niece (or nephew).

2. Assign sex characters to the vertices in the graph in Figure 5.4.9 in all possible ways.

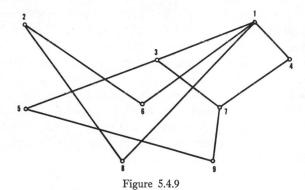

Figure 5.4.9

3. Draw the configurations which are excluded from a family tree by the taboos against marriages between: (a) half-brothers and half-sisters; (b) grandparents and grandchild; (c) uncle or aunt with niece or nephew.

CHAPTER SIX

Questions Concerning Games and Puzzles

6.1 Puzzles and Directed Graphs

Previously (Section 2.6) we explained how puzzle problems can be formulated in terms of graphs. The positions in a puzzle correspond to the vertices of the graph; the edges of the graph correspond to the possible moves from one position to another. The solution of the puzzle consists in finding a path from a given initial position to one or possibly more terminal or winning positions.

In dealing with these puzzles we used undirected graphs. This was based upon the tacit assumption that the moves could be made both ways from one position to another. Such a procedure was permissible for the puzzles of the ferryman, the three jealous husbands, and the moves of the knight on the chessboard.

But for many puzzles the moves can only be made in one direction, and in this case we are compelled to use directed graphs in the representation. If some moves can be made in both directions one can include an edge for each direction or one can use a mixed graph in which these edges are undirected. To solve the puzzle one must find a directed path from the initial position in the graph to the desired terminal position.

We shall illustrate these remarks by considering an ancient and familiar puzzle. One has three jugs A, B, C with capacities 8, 5, 3 quarts, respectively. The jug A is filled with wine and one wishes to divide the wine into two equal parts by pouring it from one container to another, that is, without using any measuring devices other than these jugs.

We shall use the following scheme for solving this puzzle graphically. To every distribution of wine in jugs B and C, we assign the pair of numbers (b, c), b denoting the amount in jug B and c the amount in jug C. Initially (b, c) has the value $(0, 0)$ and the desired terminal distribution is $(4, 0)$; jugs A and B would then contain equal amounts of the wine and jug C would be empty.

Since to every pair of real numbers (b, c) we may assign a point with coordinates (b, c) in a coordinate plane, we may think of all possible distributions as points, and these will be the vertices of our graph. It is clear from the statement of the problem that we cannot accurately pour fractions of quarts into jugs B and C; so, at best, b can take the values $0, 1, 2, 3, 4, 5$ and c the values $0, 1, 2, 3$. This means that there are $6 \times 4 = 24$ possible distinct pairs (b, c), i.e. 24 vertices in our graph. Whenever it is possible to change a known distribution (b_0, c_0) to a new distribution (b_1, c_1) by pouring wine in accurate amounts, we connect the vertex (b_0, c_0) to the vertex (b_1, c_1) by a directed edge. In our example, the edges IA_1 and IA_2 (Figure 6.1.1) lead away from the initial vertex $I: (0, 0)$. From A_1 it is possible to reach the distributions $A_{11}: (5, 3)$ and $A_{12}: (2, 3)$; and from A_2, $A_{21}: (3, 0)$ and $A_{22}: (5, 3)$ can be reached. Next, we might list all vertices attainable from these by the rules of our game and continue in this way. If the terminal vertex $T:$ $(4, 0)$ can be reached at all, this method must eventually lead to it. In fact, there may be many paths from I to T, and we may want to select the "best" solution (in the sense of having to pour wine as few times as possible) by determining a path from I to T with as few edges as possible.

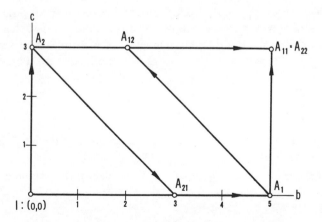

Figure 6.1.1

While from a certain initial vertex I many paths may lead to a given vertex T, there are, in general, other vertices U that cannot be reached from I by the prescribed rules. In our example, these unattainable vertices U are

$$U: \quad (1,1), \quad (1,2), \quad (2,1), \quad (2,2), \quad (3,1), \quad (3,2), \quad (4,1), \quad (4,2).$$

In other words, of the 24 vertices initially included as "possible" distributions, 8 cannot be attained, and only 16 turn out to be possible.

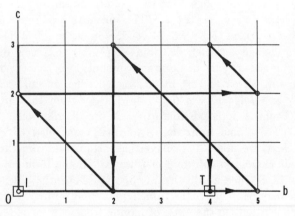

Figure 6.1.2

Actually, our solution of this jug puzzle (Figure 6.1.2) is not a very good illustration of the directed path method because all pourings can be reversed as you may check quite readily. However, if we had started with a different distribution, say one quart of wine in each of jugs B and C, i.e. from the vertex $(1, 1)$, all edges would have been directed away from $(1, 1)$.

Problem Set 6.1

1. Show that one can never pass from any distribution of the set U to another by repeated pourings.

2. Plot the points of U in Figure 6.1.2. What does their location indicate?

3. Solve the same problems for some other sizes of the jugs, for instance $A = 12$, $B = 7$, $C = 4$.

6.2 The Theory of Games

A puzzle is a solitary struggle against the difficulties inherent in a problem while in a game one plays against a human opponent. Since we have entered upon the field of entertainment and discussed some puzzles, let us also make some general observations about games. The theory of two-person games has in recent years become an important field of mathematical research. It has applications to many problems of a practical nature; we may mention engineering and economics where the theory of games is used to solve questions concerning the most effective or most economical way of performing certain complicated tasks.

Here we have no occasion to study the general theory of games. We shall only indicate how our directed graphs may be used to bring forth the principles of those games in which the moves do not depend on chance. Chess is an excellent example of what we have in mind; so is checkers, and even the simple-minded tic-tac-toe falls in this category.

In these games we have, as usual, certain positions corresponding to the vertices, and certain moves from one position to another corresponding to the directed edges. But in each position we must also know which of the two players A^* and B^* has the move. Therefore, it seems natural to divide the positions into two groups, called A and B, so that the moves are represented by directed edges from A to B or from B to A. The same position may possibly occur both in A and B.

The play then actually consists in A^* moving to a new position along an edge to B and B^* back to A. We could say that this is a game with a single piece which is moved along the directed edges back and forth between the two sets. In each position each player, presumably, knows what he wants to do. Thus we could even do away with the players if each had recorded in a book of strategy what move he would select under given conditions. As a consequence, the whole game is determined when one knows its graph, that is, the moves permitted in the game and the strategy of the players.

To win a game A^* must move from an initial position along a directed path, in part determined by B^*, to some winning position w_A in B; similarly, in order for B^* to win his last move must be to a winning position w_B in A.

A draw or undecided game may occur in two ways. There may be certain end positions in A or B which are called draws, and there are no further edges from them. A stalemate in chess is a good example. Another type of draw occurs when the game can go on indefinitely, usually by a repetition of some circuit of moves. To avoid this one may stipulate that the game is over after a certain number of repetitions of the same moves. In chess the game is drawn after the same moves have been repeated in sequence three times; the game is also limited by the rule that in 50 moves a pawn must have been moved.

We now have a perfectly good picture of a game. There remains only one essential point: When can A^* (or B^*) play in such a way that he is certain of winning? This is a question which may also be answered from the graph. The best way to handle it is to reason backward from the final winning positions for A^*. Since these positions are losing for B^* we indicate this by denoting the set of them by $L_0(B)$. In A there are some positions with edges or moves into $L_0(B)$. From such a position A^* can win in a single move; we call this set $W_1(A)$. Next there will be a set $L_1(B)$ of positions either in $L_0(B)$ or having only moves to positions in $W_1(A)$. When B^* has such a position he has either already lost or cannot avoid losing in one move. We can therefore just as well consider the larger set $L_1(B)$ as the set of lost positions for B^* (Figure 6.2.1).

We can continue this process of enlarging the losing set for B^*. There will be a certain set $W_2(A) \supseteq W_1(A)$ of vertices in A with edges to $L_1(B)$. From such positions A^* can win in at most 2 moves. Furthermore, there will be a certain set $L_2(B)$ of positions from which all edges go to $W_2(A)$ and B cannot avoid losing in at most 2 moves. When repeated this leads to two sequences of sets in A and B, respectively:

$$W_1(A) \subseteq W_2(A) \subseteq \cdots,$$

$$L_0(B) \subseteq L_1(B) \subseteq \cdots,$$

such that when A^* has a position in $W_k(A)$ he can win in k moves or less. Thus when A^* has an original position lying in some $W_k(A)$ he can always win; if this is not the case B^* must always struggle to prevent A^* from achieving a position in such a set. The winning positions for B can be found in the same way, and in the remaining ones a draw can always be achieved.

In principle this whole discussion is perfectly fine and it shows how a little graph theory may be used to analyze all game positions. If it were always practicable all these games between two persons would be reduced to a triviality, a sort of tic-tac-toe where one would always know what is a bad move and what is a good one. Fortunately, there is no likelihood that, for instance, our beloved game of chess will suffer this dismal fate.

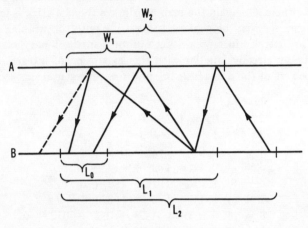

Figure 6.2.1

The number of positions in a chess game is so enormous that even our largest capacity computers are not likely to make a dent in the reputation of chess as the preeminent game of intellectual skill. The experiences from master tournaments seem to indicate that the white pieces have an advantage, but whether this is a winning position in the sense that a superbrain could always bring them to victory is a question which probably will remain unanswered forever.

We conclude with a couple of simple examples. In the first game there is a pile of matches on the table. The players A^* and B^* move in turn by picking a number of matches, say from 1 to 5, from the heap. The winner is the player who takes the last match. A^* can reach the winning position 0 when there are $W_1(A) = 1, 2, 3, 4, 5$ matches left. Only in one position—when there are 6 matches—is B^* compelled to play into $W_1(A)$. In turn, this number 6 can be reached by A^* when there are 7, 8, 9, 10, 11 matches left. Therefore, the set $W_2(A)$ consists of all numbers from 1 to 11 with 6 excluded, while $L_2(B) = 0, 6, 12$. By continuing this way one concludes that A^* can win from all numbers not divisible by 6. In the first move he leaves a number of matches divisible by 6 and in each subsequent move he takes a number of matches such that they together with those just taken by B^* add up to 6. If the number of matches in the original pile is divisible by 6, and if A^* makes the first move, B^* can always win in a similar fashion.

Our second example deals with the ancient Chinese game of Nim. In its simplest form, there are three piles of playing sticks on the table. In each move a player selects a pile and takes at least one stick from it; he may take them all. Again the man who takes the last stick is the winner. In this case we shall be content to describe only the winning positions. This is an exercise in representing numbers in the binary system. You are probably already familiar with this expansion of integers according to the powers of the number 2; the first few representations are

$$1 = (1)$$
$$2 = (1, 0) = 1 \cdot 2 + 0$$
$$3 = (1, 1) = 1 \cdot 2 + 1$$
$$4 = (1, 0, 0) = 1 \cdot 2^2 + 0 \cdot 2 + 0$$
$$5 = (1, 0, 1) = 1 \cdot 2^2 + 0 \cdot 2 + 1$$
$$6 = (1, 1, 0) = 1 \cdot 2^2 + 1 \cdot 2 + 0$$
$$7 = (1, 1, 1) = 1 \cdot 2^2 + 1 \cdot 2 + 1$$
$$8 = (1, 0, 0, 0) = 1 \cdot 2^3 + 0 \cdot 2^2 + 0 \cdot 2 + 0$$
$$9 = (1, 0, 0, 1) = 1 \cdot 2^3 + 0 \cdot 2^2 + 0 \cdot 2 + 1$$
$$10 = (1, 0, 1, 0) = 1 \cdot 2^3 + 0 \cdot 2^2 + 1 \cdot 2 + 0.$$

Less familiar is the *digital addition* which one can perform on these representations. To see how it works we consider the following two examples:

```
  1 0 1 1              1 1 1 1
    1 0 1                1 1 0
    1 1 0                  1 1
  1 1 0 0            ───────────
───────────            1 0 1 0
  0 1 0 0
```

We add columnwise as in ordinary addition, but in the sum we write a 0 in a given column if there is an even number of ones and a 1 if there is an odd number. As you see, this process is different from ordinary addition in the binary system.

Now back to our game of Nim. For any position we find the digital sum of the three numbers in the heaps. When the distributions are 13, 12, 7, or 14, 11, 5, the respective sums are

```
  1 1 0 1              1 1 1 0
  1 1 0 0              1 0 1 1
    1 1 1                1 0 1
───────────          ───────────
  0 1 1 0              0 0 0 0
```

We call a position a *zero-position* if the digital sum contains only zeros as in the second example; otherwise we have a *regular position*. The winning positions for A^* are the regular positions; he loses in the zero-positions.

The proof is simple. When A^* is in a regular position he can take out a number of sticks such that he leaves a zero-position for B^*. This he can do by selecting a heap whose number has a 1 in the column of the first 1 in the sum; from this heap he removes a number of sticks so calculated that the new digital sum is zero. For instance, in our first example we may select the heap with $14 = (1, 1, 0, 1)$ sticks and change it into $11 = (1, 0, 1, 1)$. In this particular case we could also have taken sticks from either one of the two other heaps; changing 12 to $10 = (1, 0, 1, 0)$ or 7 to $1 = (0, 0, 0, 1)$ would have accomplished our aim just as well.

When A^* has placed B^* into a zero-position anything that B^* does will bring A^* back into a regular position; for, any number of sticks that B^* removes will change at least one of the digits in one of the numbers and hence in the digital sum. The game will finally end by A^* bringing B^* into the smallest zero-position when all piles are empty. As one sees, the situation is somewhat similar to that in the first example.

It is clear that the same method can be applied when there are more than three heaps. Let us observe also that in discussing Nim we did not start with the empty position and work backward to find the winning positions. This could have been done and with the same result, of course. However, it was easier to make use of the fact that the solution was known and just to verify that it was correct.

Problem Set 6.2

1. Play a game of Nim with one of your friends (or enemies).

2. Determine the first winning and losing sets $W_1(A)$, $W_2(A)$, $L_1(B)$, $L_2(B)$ in Nim.

3. Examine the following game: There are 2 heaps of matches and each player has the choice of taking a match from one or the other, or one from each. The winner takes the last match or matches. Find the sets $W_1(A)$, $W_2(A)$, $L_1(B)$, $L_2(B)$. Can you find a general rule for the winning positions?

6.3 The Sportswriter's Paradox

After the football season is all over, and when the incidents of the games, the peculiarities of teams and players, have been hashed and rehashed until the subject is exhausted, some newspaperman almost always brings up the startling fact that the strongest team was not the supermen of Superb College (S), but rather the dismal group from Rien du Tout (R). This he demonstrates by exhibiting a sequence of games in which R actually won over A, then A over B, and so on until S is reached at the end of the line.

To analyze when such directed arcs can be found let us consider the case where there are n teams or contestants

$$(6.3.1) \hspace{3cm} A_1, \quad A_2, \quad \cdots, \quad A_n$$

who have all played against each other. To simplify, we assume that there are no draws. The graph picture is therefore a complete graph (Section 1.2) in which each pair of n vertices is connected by a directed edge. Our first result is

THEOREM 6.1. *In a complete directed graph there is always a directed arc passing through all vertices.*

PROOF. It is sufficient to show that if we have a directed arc

$$(6.3.2) \hspace{2cm} \rho = (A_1, A_2)(A_2, A_3)\cdots(A_{k-1}, A_k)$$

passing through some of the vertices (6.3.1) then we can always find a directed arc which passes through one more vertex. So let us add an arbitrary vertex A_{k+1} to those already in ρ in (6.3.2) and consider the various possible directions of the edges connecting A_{k+1} to the vertices in ρ.

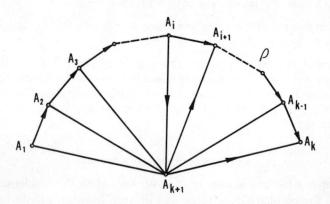

Figure 6.3.1

If there is an edge directed from A_k to A_{k+1} we can continue ρ to A_{k+1}. We suppose therefore that the edge (A_{k+1}, A_k) is directed from A_{k+1} (see Figure 6.3.1) and we look, consecutively, at the edges connecting A_{k+1} to A_{k-1}, A_{k-2}, $\cdots$, A_1. Suppose that at least one of these edges is directed toward A_{k+1}, and let (A_i, A_{k+1}) be the first such edge we come to in the sequence (A_{k+1}, A_{k-1}), (A_{k+1}, A_{k-2}), $\cdots$, (A_{k+1}, A_{i+1}), (A_i, A_{k+1}). Then, clearly there will be a pair of consecutive edges

(6.3.3) (A_i, A_{k+1}), (A_{k+1}, A_{i+1}),

the first directed from A_i to A_{k+1} and the second directed from A_{k+1} to A_{i+1}. In this case there is the directed arc

$$A_1, \cdots, A_i, A_{k+1}, A_{i+1}, \cdots, A_k.$$

There remains the case where all edges are directed from A_{k+1} to ρ. Then one can begin an arc through the edge (A_{k+1}, A_1) and continue through ρ. This is the only instance where it is necessary to change the initial vertex of the arc.

This result shows that after the tournament is completed one can always arrange the contestants in a directed victory path. The theorem, however, does not quite solve what we had in mind with regard to the sportswriters' paradox. Here it was required to take some fixed vertex A_1 and draw a directed path from it through all the other vertices. This does not follow from the preceding argument since in enlarging the arc ρ we might be compelled to change its initial vertex.

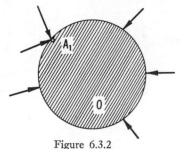

Figure 6.3.2

In fact, one cannot always find such an arc. This is evident when A_1 is an *outclassed individual*, that is, one who has had nothing but losses in the tournament. More generally, such an arc from A_1 cannot be found if A_1 belongs to an *outclassed group* O whose members have competed, so to speak, only among themselves because no member was able to achieve a victory over an outside opponent (Figure 6.3.2). In the graph representation this means that there are only directed edges pointing towards O and none pointing away from O. But we can show:

THEOREM 6.2. *If A_1 does not belong to an outclassed group there is always a directed path from A_1 through all vertices.*

PROOF. We construct an arc ρ from A_1 as in (6.3.2), making it as long as possible. The proof of Theorem 6.1 shows that if there is any vertex A_{k+1} to which there is directed an incoming edge from ρ then ρ can be enlarged without changing the initial vertex A_1. Thus when ρ cannot be enlarged its vertices form an outclassed group; but since A_1 does not belong to an outclassed group ρ must run through all vertices.

Our theorem shows that when there are no outclassed groups there are directed arcs through all vertices from any initial vertex. More specific is the next

THEOREM 6.3. *If a directed complete graph has no outclassed groups there is a directed circuit through all vertices.*

PROOF. If ρ is an arc through all vertices to the endpoint A_n then there must also be outgoing edges from A_n since it cannot be an outclassed vertex. Such an edge (A_n, A_i) must go to a previous vertex A_i on ρ so that we are certain that there is some directed circuit (Figure 6.3.3).

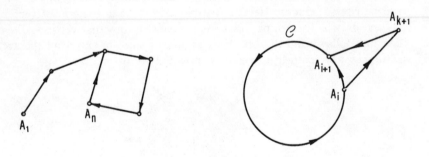

Figure 6.3.3   Figure 6.3.4

Let

$$\mathcal{C} = (A_1, A_2) \cdots (A_{k-1}, A_k)(A_k, A_1)$$

be some such directed circuit which does not include all vertices. Suppose there is some vertex A_{k+1} such that there are edges between $\mathcal{C}$ and A_{k+1} in both directions. Then as in (6.3.3) there will be adjacent edges to $\mathcal{C}$ in both directions and one can enlarge $\mathcal{C}$ by replacing the edge (A_i, A_{i+1}) by (A_i, A_{k+1}) and (A_{k+1}, A_{i+1}). (See Figure 6.3.4.)

This leaves us with the case where the vertices outside of $\mathcal{C}$ fall into two types: Vertices M from which all edges are directed to $\mathcal{C}$ and vertices N from which all edges are directed from $\mathcal{C}$. There must be vertices of both these types, for if there were no vertices M the set $\{N\}$ of all vertices N would form an outclassed group, while if there were no vertices N the vertices in $\mathcal{C}$ would be such a group. (See Figure 6.3.5.)

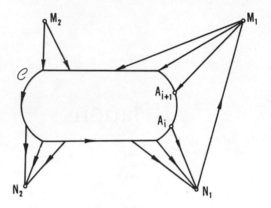

Figure 6.3.5

The vertices in the set $\{M\}$ will be connected by edges to the set $\{N\}$. There must be at least one edge (N_1, M_1) from a vertex N_1 in $\{N\}$ to a vertex M_1 in $\{M\}$, for otherwise the set $\{N\}$ would be outclassed. But then one can again enlarge $\mathcal{C}$ by replacing the edge (A_i, A_{i+1}) by the three edges

$$(A_i, N_1)(N_1, M_1)(M_1, A_{i+1}).$$

In this manner we can steadily enlarge $\mathcal{C}$ until it includes all vertices.

Problem Set 6.3

1. Get the score sheet for some round-robin chess tournament. Find a directed arc passing through all vertices in the graph. Examine whether there are any outclassed sets; if not, try to find a directed circuit passing through all vertices.

2. How must the preceding discussion be modified when draws are allowed?

CHAPTER SEVEN

Relations

7.1 Relations and Graphs

So far we have discussed a variety of uses of graphs. Applications to everyday problems and to games and puzzles were considered. Our choice of topics had the advantage that we could deal with well known and simple concepts. In this chapter we shall strive to make clear that graphs are closely related to, indeed, are only a different way of formulating, some of the most fundamental concepts of mathematics in general.

A mathematical system, as we usually encounter it, consists of a set of objects or elements. For instance, we deal commonly with numbers and these may belong to more or less general types; we may discuss the set of integers, the positive numbers, the rational numbers, real numbers, imaginary numbers, complex numbers. In algebra we are concerned with elements which can be added, subtracted, multiplied, and so on. In geometry we ordinarily have before us a set of points or special categories of points like straight lines, circles, planes, etc. In logic we deal with the properties of statements of various kinds.

To construct a mathematical theory we need more than these elements; we need *relations* between them. Let us illustrate this: In the case of numbers we have equal numbers a and b; in formal mathematical terminology we write $a = b$. We have numbers a and b which are different, and write $a \neq b$. The symbol $a > b$ denotes that a is greater than b;

similarly $a \geq b$ means that a is either greater than b or equal to b. When we deal with integers and a divides b we write $a \mid b$.

In geometry, two objects, say triangles A and B, may be congruent, in which case we write $A \cong B$; or one may include the other and we write $A \supset B$. Two straight lines may be parallel, $A \parallel B$, or they may be orthogonal (intersecting in a right angle), $A \perp B$. In logic one statement or assertion may imply another, $A \rightarrow B$. In set theory the relation $a \in S$ between an element a and a set S means that a is an element of the set S.

All of these relations concern two objects and therefore they are often called *binary relations*, or simply *relations* (for short). There are other relations; for instance, a *ternary relation* concerns three objects. As an example of such a relation we may take: A lies between B and C.

The importance of relations in mathematics makes it necessary to arrive at a general definition for them. For a general (binary) relation with the symbol R we write

$$(7.1.1) \qquad\qquad aRb$$

and say that b *is in the relation R to a*. This shall mean that b belongs to some special set R_a which is determined for each a by the relation. So, for instance, the relation $a > b$ means that b belongs to the set of all numbers which are less than a. For integers a and b the relation $a \mid b$ or a divides b means that b belongs to the set of all integers which are multiples of a. Therefore, in general (7.1.1) is another way of expressing that b belongs to the set R_a which R associates with a.

Let us return to our graphs. Actually, each directed graph G defines a relation in its vertex set. This relation we may write

$$(7.1.2) \qquad\qquad aGb$$

and it signifies that there is a directed edge from a to b in G. The corresponding set $R_a = G_a$, associated with a under the relation, is then the set of all those vertices b in G to which there is an edge from a. Thus, to state that there is an edge (a, b) in G is the same as saying that the relation (7.1.2) holds.

As a consequence we might be inclined to consider the theory of graphs as a special part of the theory of relations. Actually the two theories are co-extensive. Suppose that a relation R is defined in a set S so that there is a set R_a associated with each a in S. Then one can construct a graph G for R simply by drawing an edge from a to each vertex in R_a (Figure 7.1.1).

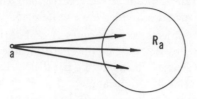

Figure 7.1.1

Since the theory of relations and the theory of graphs are only different aspects of the same concepts one may ask why mathematicians
maintain a distinction between them. This is partly due to habit and
tradition, just as in analytic geometry one talks about a straight line
while in algebra the same concept is a linear equation in two unknowns.
But there is actually a difference in the methods of the two disciplines,
although not a sharp one, of course. The reason is that in relations one
deals mostly with infinite sets R_a; as an example take the relation $a > b$
for all real numbers. This means that in the corresponding graph picture
there should be an infinite number of vertices and an infinite number of
edges from each vertex. It is extremely difficult to have any intuitive
perception of the properties of such a graph. When we discussed graph
problems in the preceding it was of great help to be able to reason geo-
metrically about the vertices and edges connecting them. For many
types of relations these arguments lose their lucid character; indeed, they
may not be valid for infinitely many elements and so one is forced to
introduce other types of proofs for relations in infinite sets.

Problem Set 7.1

1. List some relations other than those mentioned. Try to make up some of
   your own.

2. For the set of numbers 2, 3, 4, 5, 6 draw the graphs and list the sets R_x
   for each of the relations:

   $\quad$ a) $\; x > y, \qquad$ b) $\; x \neq y, \qquad$ c) $\; x \mid y.$

7.2 Special Conditions

New points of view usually produce new observations. There are certain
aspects of relation theory which should also be introduced in graph theory
to make the parallelism more complete.

For any relation R it may happen that an element is in this relation to itself:

(7.2.1) aRa.

For instance, a line A is said to be parallel to itself: $A \parallel A$; a number
satisfies $a \geq a$, and so on. In graphs we have so far made no provision
for this special case. It should correspond to an edge (a, a) having both
endpoints the same. Therefore, we introduce *loops* (a, a) in the graph
picture; this is an edge returning to itself at the vertex a (Figure 7.2.1)

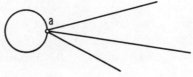

Figure 7.2.1

A relation R such that (7.2.1) holds for every a we call a *reflexive
relation*. In the graph picture this means that there is a loop at every
vertex. As examples we have as above the relation for lines: $A \parallel B$; or
for numbers: $a \geq b$.

If the relation (7.2.1) does not hold for any element we say that R is
an *antireflexive relation*. This is equivalent to the property that the corresponding graph has no vertices with loops. As an example we take the
relation for orthogonal lines: $A \perp B$; that is, A and B intersect at an
angle of 90°.

To any relation R we can define a *converse relation* R^* by writing
bR^*a whenever aRb holds. So, for instance, the relation $a \mid b$, that is,
a divides b, has for its converse relation

$$b \mid^* a,$$

or b is a multiple of a. Frequently there is a special symbol for R^*: The
relation a is greater than b, $a > b$, has the converse $b < a$, or b is less
than a. The relation $a \in A$, a is an element of A, has for its converse
$A \supset a$, or A contains a.

The definition of the converse relation shows that if there is an edge
(a, b) in the graph G corresponding to R then there is an edge (b, a) in
the graph G^* corresponding to R^*. In other words, G^* is the *converse
graph* to G, that is, the same graph but with oppositely directed edges.

It may happen that for a relation R one has simultaneously

(7.2.2)　　　　　　　　aRb　　and　　bRa

for a pair of elements a and b. In the graph picture one should then have two edges

$$(a, b)　　\text{and}　　(b, a),$$

one in each direction. But in graphs one can replace such a pair by a single edge without direction, just as in the case of two-way streets.

Some relations have the property that one of the relations (7.2.2) always implies the other; such relations are called *symmetric*. As examples let us mention the parallel relation, $A \parallel B$, the orthogonal relation, $A \perp B$, and the equality relation, $A = B$. According to the remarks we just made one can say:

A symmetric relation has a graph with undirected edges; conversely a graph with undirected edges defines a symmetric relation.

There are some relations R in which one of the relations (7.7.2) can never hold when the other is satisfied. As an example take $a > b$. Such relations are called *antisymmetric* or *asymmetric*. Their graphs have no undirected or two-way edges between any two vertices; furthermore, there are no loops, that is, these relations are antireflexive.

There is another property which plays an important role in relation theory. We say that a relation R is *transitive* if the two conditions

$$aRb　　\text{and}　　bRc$$

imply

$$aRc.$$

Among the examples let us list the relations: A parallel B, $A \parallel B$; a is equal to b, $a = b$; a greater than b, $a > b$; a divides b, $a \mid b$. On the other hand the relations $A \perp B$ and $a \neq b$ are not transitive.

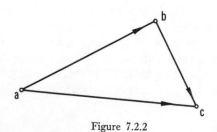

Figure 7.2.2

A transitive relation has the following characteristic graph property: For any pair of edges

(7.2.3) $(a, b), (b, c)$

there exists a *resultant* edge (a, c) (Figure 7.2.2).

By repeated use of this property one concludes that when there is a directed path from a vertex x to another y then there is also an edge (x, y).

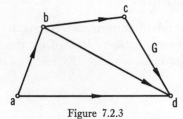
Figure 7.2.3

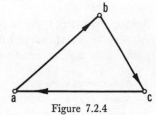
Figure 7.2.4

Suppose finally that we have a graph G with directed edges which is not transitive. For example, the graph in Figure 7.2.3 has no edge between the vertices a and c. The graph in Figure 7.2.4 has an edge (c, a), while the resultant edge of (a, b) and (b, c) would be the edge (a, c). In any case, one can always make a directed graph G transitive by adding directed edges until for each pair of consecutive edges the resultant has been included. The new graph G^T so obtained is called the *transitive closure* of G. Figures 7.2.5 and 7.2.6 show the transitive closures of the graphs in Figures 7.2.3 and 7.2.4, respectively. Observe that when the resultants (a, c) of (a, b) and (b, c); (c, b) of (c, a) and (a, b); and (b, a) of (b, c) and (c, a) are added to the graph in Figure 7.2.3, the transitive closure so obtained is the graph of a symmetric relation.

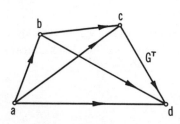

Figure 7.2.5

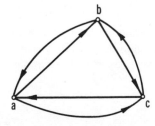
Figure 7.2.6

Problem Set 7.2

1. Examine some other relations with respect to the properties mentioned above.

2. Examine the family relations:
   a) A is a descendant of B.   b) A and B have a common forefather.

3. Form the transitive closures of the graphs in Figure 5.1.1 and Figure 5.1.2.

7.3   Equivalence Relations

Among the many types of mathematical relations the equivalence relations play an outstanding role. An *equivalence relation*, denoted by the symbol $\sim$, is characterized by three properties:

1. *Reflexivity*: $a \sim a$.
2. *Symmetry*: $a \sim b$ implies $b \sim a$.
3. *Transitivity*: $a \sim b$ and $b \sim c$ implies $a \sim c$.

An example which comes to mind immediately is equality: $a = b$. Indeed, the equivalence relations have properties similar to equality and in many instances one considers an equivalence as a new kind of equality; a good example is geometric congruence $A \cong B$ for two figures.

In number theory one uses another type of equivalence relation which is also called a *congruence*. When a, b and m are three integers one writes

$$(7.3.1) \qquad\qquad a \equiv b \; (\mathrm{mod}\; m)$$

whenever the difference $a - b$ is divisible by m, or in other words, when

$$(7.3.2) \qquad\qquad a = b + km$$

where k is some integer.

In number theory one expresses the relation (7.3.1) in words as follows: The number a is congruent to b for the modulus m ("modulus" means little measure). As examples let us take

$$11 \equiv 2 \; (\mathrm{mod}\; 3)$$

$$-7 \equiv 19 \; (\mathrm{mod}\; 13).$$

For systematic reasons one uses this notation (7.3.1) also in cases where we commonly use other terms. For instance, the congruences

$$b \equiv 0 \ (\text{mod } 2), \qquad c \equiv 1 \ (\text{mod } 2)$$

mean, respectively, that b is an even number and that c is an odd number. Also,

$$a \equiv 0 \ (\text{mod } m)$$

means that a is divisible by m.

To prove that a congruence (7.3.1) satisfies the three conditions for an equivalence relation is quite simple.

1. $a \equiv a \ (\text{mod } m)$ since $a = a + 0m$.

2. If $a \equiv b \ (\text{mod } m)$ then by (7.3.2) we have $a = b + km$ which is the same as $b = a + (-k)m$, so that also $b \equiv a \ (\text{mod } m)$.

3. If $a \equiv b \ (\text{mod } m)$ and also $b \equiv c \ (\text{mod } m)$ then by (7.3.2)

$$a = b + km, \qquad b = c + lm,$$

and therefore

$$a = c + lm + km = c + (l + k)m$$

so that $a \equiv c \ (\text{mod } m)$.

For $m = 0$ the congruence (7.3.1) reduces to an ordinary equality $a = b$, according to (7.3.2).

An equivalence relation can also be interpreted in a different manner as we shall now see. First we notice that an equivalence relation is always defined for the elements of some set S; two elements are either equivalent or non-equivalent. In the congruence relation in (7.3.1) we deal with the set S of all integers. The parallel relation $A \parallel B$ is an equivalence relation defined for the set of all straight lines in the plane or in space.

Suppose an equivalence relation $a \sim b$ is defined for the elements in a set S. Consider all elements b equivalent to a. These elements form a set B_a which is a part of S. These sets B_a correspond to the relation sets R_a we introduced earlier for general relations, but in this case we prefer to call them the *equivalence blocks* of our equivalence relation.

What are the properties of these blocks? Since the relation is reflexive, $a \sim a$, the equivalence block B_a of a contains a. Suppose now that b is an element in B_a, that is, $a \sim b$, and let c be an element in the equivalence block B_b of b, that is, $b \sim c$ (Figure 7.3.1). Since the relation is transitive we obtain $a \sim c$, so c belongs to B_a. This means that the whole equivalence block B_b is contained in B_a. But if $a \sim b$ then $b \sim a$ since the relation is symmetric; so we conclude in the same manner that B_a is contained in B_b. This shows that $B_a = B_b$ if $a \sim b$.

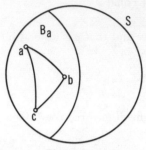

Figure 7.3.1

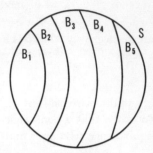

Figure 7.3.2

Next take two elements a and b in S that are not equivalent. One often uses the notation $a \nsim b$, striking out the equivalence symbol. In this case the two blocks B_a and B_b are *disjoint*, that is, they have no elements in common. For, if an element c belonged both to B_a and B_b it would follow that

$$a \sim c, \quad \text{and} \quad b \sim c,$$

and so $a \sim b$, contrary to assumption.

Since each element belongs to just one of the blocks, we have decomposed the whole set S into a sum of disjoint equivalence blocks (Figure 7.3.2). Each block consists of a set of equivalent elements.

As an example let us take first the family S of all straight lines in the plane and the relation $A \parallel B$; here each equivalence block or class consists of all lines having the same *direction*.

Secondly, the number theory congruence (7.3.1) divides all integers into equivalence blocks; these are called *residue classes* (mod m). Each class consists, respectively, of the numbers

$$B_0 = km, \quad B_1 = 1 + km, \quad B_2 = 2 + km, \quad \cdots, \quad B_{m-1} = m - 1 + km.$$

In other words, B_r consists of the numbers which leave the remainder r when divided by m. For $m = 2$ we find the division of the integers into even and odd numbers; when $m = 3$ we have the three different types of numbers

$$3k, \quad 1 + 3k, \quad 2 + 3k.$$

We saw that an equivalence relation defined a decomposition of all elements in the set S into disjoint blocks as in Figure 7.3.2. But suppose conversely that we have some such decomposition of S into sets B_i without common elements. In mathematics this is usually called a *partition* of the set S. Then we can define an equivalence relation in S simply by putting $a \sim b$ whenever a and b belong to the same set B. It is evident that the three conditions for an equivalence are satisfied. This shows that an equivalence relation and a partition or decomposition of the set S into disjoint parts are in reality two aspects of the same thing. Each equivalence gives a disjoint decomposition and each such decomposition defines a unique equivalence.

Let us take a non-mathematical illustration. Two individuals have the same nationality if they are citizens of the same state; conversely the nationalities divide humans into classes (excluding the stateless, who constitute a separate class).

Let us not forget a third aspect of equivalence relations: their graphs. When S is taken to be a set of vertices, all those vertices which belong to a block B_i should be connected by edges so that we obtain a complete graph G_i for each B_i; in addition, there is a loop at each vertex. There are no edges connecting two different blocks so that the graph G of the whole relation has the graphs G_i for its connected components.

In Figure 7.3.3 we have drawn the graph of an equivalence relation in a set with 12 elements; the blocks contain respectively 5, 4, 2, 1 elements.

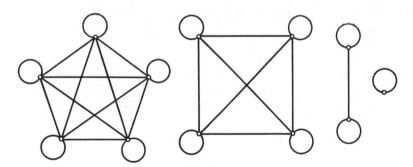

Figure 7.3.3

Problem Set 7.3

1. Find other examples of equivalence relations.

2. Prove that the congruences (7.3.1) can be added, subtracted, multiplied: If

$$a \equiv b \pmod{m} \quad \text{and} \quad c \equiv d \pmod{m}$$

then

$$a \pm c \equiv b \pm d \pmod{m}, \quad ac \equiv bd \pmod{m}.$$

3. Two real numbers (also complex numbers) are called associated when they have the same absolute value $|a| = |b|$. Show that this is an equivalence relation and determine the elements in each block.

7.4 Partial Order

To illustrate another type of basic mathematical relation we suppose that we have a set S of elements of some kind. For instance, these elements may be numbers, points, or even the human beings in the world. Within this set S we consider some family of smaller sets or subsets $A, B, \cdots$. If for instance S consists of all the real numbers each subset in our family may be the numbers in a certain interval; if S is the set of points in the plane the sets $A, B, \cdots$ may be all points on given lines or figures.

For such subsets we have an inclusion relation $A \supseteq B$ which may or may not be fulfilled for a pair of our sets; it signifies that all elements in B also belong to A. The two sets may have the same elements so that $A = B$. One sees immediately that the following three conditions are fulfilled for an

Inclusion relation

1. Reflexivity: $A \supseteq A$
2. Transitivity: If $A \supseteq B$ and $B \supseteq C$, then $A \supseteq C$.
3. Identification: $A \supseteq B$ and $B \supseteq A$ implies $A = B$.

Instead of using the relation $A \supseteq B$ one often applies the *strict inclusion relation* denoted by $A \supset B$. This expresses as before that B is a part or subset of A, but the possibility $A = B$ is excluded so that B is a *proper subset* of A. In this case we have the properties:

Strict inclusion relation

1. Anti-reflexivity: $A \supset A$ cannot occur.
2. Transitivity: $A \supset B$ and $B \supset C$ implies $A \supset C$.

A binary relation $a \geq b$ which satisfies the conditions for an inclusion relation is called a *partial order*. It satisfies therefore the axioms:

1. $a \geq a$
2. If $a \geq b$ and $b \geq c$, then $a \geq c$.
3. $a \geq b$ and $b \geq a$ implies $a = b$.

In the various branches of mathematics one uses the inclusion symbols both in the pointed form $a \geq b$ and in the rounded form $a \supseteq b$; the latter form is often reserved for set inclusion.

In reality, partial order and set inclusion are only different formulations for the same idea. To each element a in a partial order there is a relation set R_a consisting of all the elements b for which $a \geq b$. Since the relation is reflexive a belongs to R_a. Two different elements a and b correspond to different sets R_a and R_b; for, if $R_a = R_b$ one would have simultaneously $a \geq b$, $b \geq a$, and so $a = b$. Now, as we shall show, one has $a \geq b$ if and only if one has the set inclusion $R_a \supseteq R_b$. If namely $a \geq b$ then for any element c in R_b the relation $b \geq c$ holds and so $a \geq c$, that is $R_a \supseteq R_b$. On the other hand, if $R_a \supseteq R_b$ then $a \geq b$ since b is in R_b.

In the same way one introduces *strict partial order* as a relation $a > b$ which satisfies the conditions:

1. $a > a$ is not possible.
2. $a > b$ and $b > c$ implies $a > c$.

As above one verifies that one has $a > b$ if and only if there is a strict set inclusion $R_a \supset R_b$ for the corresponding relation sets. The symbol $>$ is used here in a more general sense than in the usual "greater than" meaning for numbers.

Next we turn to the graph picture G of a partial order, particularly in the case where there is only a finite number of vertices. It is not necessary to make any particular distinction between a partial order and a strict partial order; the only difference is that the first has loops, the second not. Whenever $a > b$ there is a directed edge (a, b) in G. In Figure 7.4.1 we have drawn such a strict partial order on eight vertices.

Let us hasten to say that this is not the usual way of presenting a partial order. In the graph above, whenever there are two edges (a, b) and (b, c) there is also an edge (a, c). One can simplify the diagram by leaving out all such resultant edges. In general, whenever there is a directed arc $A(a, b)$ from a to b there should, strictly speaking, also be an edge (a, b); but since all such resultant edges are direct consequences of the existence of directed arcs, these edges may be considered to be superfluous and so they can be omitted. When these reductions are made in the graph in Figure 7.4.1 we are left with the much simpler graph shown in Figure 7.4.2.

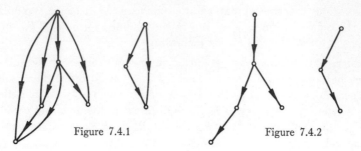

Figure 7.4.1   Figure 7.4.2

The graph of a partial order from which all loops and superfluous edges have been removed is called a *basis graph*. If $A(a, b)$ is a directed arc in the basis graph, no directed edge (a, b) can exist since it would be superfluous. Nor can there be any directed edge (b, a) in the opposite direction, for together with $A(a, b)$ it would produce a directed circuit returning to a, giving $a > a$ contrary to assumption (Figure 7.4.3). On the other hand an acyclic directed graph, that is, a directed graph without directed circuits, produces a partial order when one writes $a > b$ whenever there is a directed arc from a to b.

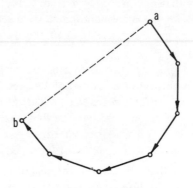

Figure 7.4.3

A (strict) *order relation* is a (strict) partial order $a > b$ which *in addition to the previous conditions* also fulfills the condition of

Completeness: For any two different elements a and b one of the relations $a > b$, $b > a$ is always satisfied. In other words, *all* elements in the set can be "compared" in an order relation. This is sometimes called a *complete order* in contradistinction to the partial orders. Analogously the order relation $a \geq b$ is defined by the same completeness condition in addition to the conditions for partial order.

In an order relation the relation sets R_a and R_b of two elements must satisfy $R_a \supset R_b$ or $R_b \supset R_a$. In mathematics as well as in everyday life one commonly deals with ordered sets, for example: Names are ordered lexicographically, that is, according to alphabetical order; boys may be ordered or rated according to height, scores, school marks or many other criteria. Most familiar in mathematics is the order of the numbers on the real number axis. Here the relation set R_a consists of all numbers b satisfying $a > b$; that is, in the usual representation, R_a consists of all numbers to the left of a on the axis (Figure 7.4.4).

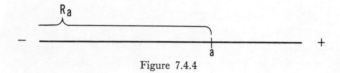

Figure 7.4.4

Very often we deal with ordered sets of a finite number of elements. Such a set contains some element a_1 smaller than all the others, a next element a_2 greater than a_1 but smaller than the others, and so on up to the greatest a_n. This means we can order the elements just as we order the integers 1, 2, $\cdots$, n according to size. In more formidable mathematical terms this would be expressed: Any ordered set with n elements is order isomorphic to the integers 1, 2, $\cdots$, n.

Problem Set 7.4

1. Draw the complete graph and the basis graph for the order of the four numbers 1, 2, 3, 4.

2. What is the basis graph for the order of the n numbers 1, 2, $\cdots$, n?

3. Prove that the division relation $a \mid b$ for integers is a partial order. What is the distinction in this case between the partial order and the strict partial order?

4. Take all subsets of a set S with three elements a, b, c. How many subsets are there? Construct the graph and the basis graph for the corresponding partial order. Why is it desirable to introduce also a void subset $\varnothing$ having no elements?

CHAPTER EIGHT

Planar Graphs

8.1 Conditions for Planar Graphs

A planar graph, as we have already explained (reread Section 1.4) is a graph which can be drawn in the plane in some manner so that the edges have no intersections except at the vertices. We also gave a number of illustrations of planar graphs. In Section 1.5 we analyzed the problem of the three houses and the three wells and explained why the corresponding graph could not be planar. The graph of the problem (Figure 1.5.1) can be drawn in many ways, as is possible for all graphs. When we say "the" graph we mean any graph isomorphic to a particular graph describing the situation. Therefore, the statement "the graph in Figure 1.5.1 is not planar" means it has no planar isomorph. For instance, the vertices may be placed in a hexagon as in Figure 8.1.1. The intersection in the center is not a vertex; the edges should be considered to pass over each other at this point.

There is even a graph with only 5 vertices which is not planar, namely the complete graph on 5 vertices (Figure 8.1.2). Why this graph cannot be planar may be made clear by reasoning similar to that used in Section 1.5 to show that the graph in Figure 8.1.1 (or Figure 1.5.1) is not planar. The vertices in any representation of the graph must lie on a circuit ρ

in some order, say $ABCDEA$. There is an edge (E, B) and in our planar graph we have the choice of putting it on the inside or the outside of ρ. The argument is similar in both cases; let us put it on the inside as in Figure 8.1.3. From A there are edges to D and C. Since edge (E, B) prevents them from being inside of ρ they must both be on the outside. The edge (D, B) can be drawn only inside ρ since the edge (A, C) blocks the access to B from the outside. But then we have no way of drawing the last edge (C, E) in the plane, for it cannot be placed inside ρ due to the edge (D, B), nor outside ρ due to the edge (A, D).

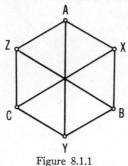

Figure 8.1.1

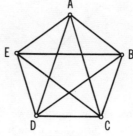

Figure 8.1.2

We have discussed the special graphs representing the three houses with the three wells (Figure 8.1.1) and the complete graph with 5 vertices (Figure 8.1.2) in some detail because they play a particular role in determining, in general, whether or not a given graph is planar. To state a criterion for planar graphs due to the Polish mathematician Kuratowski (1930), we must explain what we mean by *expanding* and *contracting* a graph.

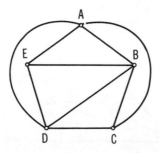

Figure 8.1.3

Suppose we add new vertices on some edges of a graph, so that these edges become arcs consisting of several edges. This operation we call *expanding* the graph. In Figure 8.1.4 we have illustrated the expansion of a graph (a) with four vertices to a graph (b).

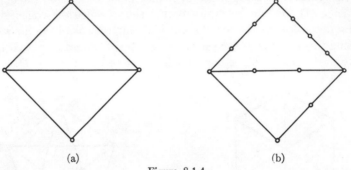

(a)   (b)

Figure 8.1.4

Conversely, suppose we have a graph as in (b) consisting of divided arcs with no edges at the intermediate vertices. By the reverse operation it can be *contracted* to a graph in which the original arcs become edges. So in Figure 8.1.4 the graph (b) can be contracted to the graph (a) by dropping the inner division vertices in the arcs. We are now able to state the theorem of Kuratowski:

A graph is planar if and only if it does not contain within it any graph which can be contracted to the pentagonal graph (Figure 8.1.2) or the hexagonal graph (Figure 8.1.1).

The proof is not very difficult, but it is somewhat involved and would require more space than we can afford here.

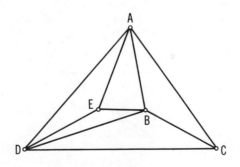

Figure 8.1.5

Let us add a few other observations about planar graphs. We tried in the preceding, for instance in Figure 1.5.2 or Figure 8.1.3, to find a planar representation of a graph by drawing its edges as more or less ingeniously bending curves. Actually, this is not essential. One can show that any planar graph can be drawn in the plane in such a manner that all edges are straight lines provided, of course, that no pair of vertices is connected by more than one edge. As an illustration we may take the graph in Figure 8.1.3 and represent it as in Figure 8.1.5.

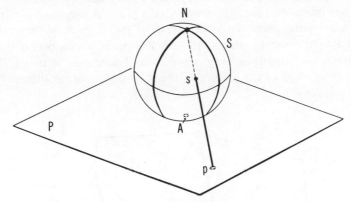

Figure 8.1.6

Another fact which should be mentioned is that any planar graph can just as well be drawn with vertices and edges lying on the surface of a sphere. There are many ways of obtaining such a representation. One can, for instance, use a stereographic projection; this is a method often introduced by cartographers, particularly for maps of regions of the earth around the poles.

Let P be the plane in which our graph is located. We place a sphere S so that it touches P, so to speak, at its Antarctic Pole A (Figure 8.1.6). The North Pole N is taken as the projection center. To any point p in the plane P we draw the line from N. This line intersects S in a point s. To each p we associate the corresponding point s on S. By the reverse procedure any graph on the sphere S can be projected back upon a plane P tangent to S; the only point on S that has no image on P is the projection center N.

Problem Set 8.1

1. Take away the edge AY in the graph in Figure 8.1.1. Draw the remaining graph in the plane with straight line, non-intersecting edges.

2. Try to find all graphs with 6 vertices which are not planar.

8.2   Euler's Formula

We shall now examine planar graphs which form a *polygonal net* in the plane. By this we mean that the edges in the planar graph G form a set of adjoining polygons in the plane, dividing it up into polygonal pieces as we have indicated in Figure 8.2.1.

To avoid any misunderstanding let us emphasize that, in contrast to ordinary usage, when we talk about polygons we do not necessarily mean that the edges are straight lines. They may be any kind of non-selfintersecting continuous curves which divide up the plane. A very good illustration of a *polygonal graph* would be a map of the U. S. A. showing the division into the various states. Indeed, any map of the border lines between various countries may serve. The boundaries between the states are the edges of the graph and the states or countries themselves are the polygons.

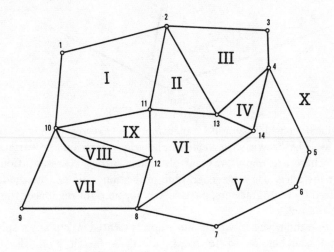

Figure 8.2.1

Now let us return to our polygonal graphs. As we have indicated, they are connected; moreover, we require that no polygon shall completely surround another. The boundary edges of a polygon form a circuit, sometimes called a *minimal circuit*. The part of the plane which it surrounds is a *face* of the graph. There is also a *maximal circuit* C_1 which surrounds the whole graph with all of its faces. A most excellent guiding principle in mathematics consists in introducing such conventions that the formulas become as simple as possible. In our case it turns out to be advantageous to consider the part of the plane lying outside of C_1 to be a face of the graph with C_1 as boundary. This we call the *infinite face*. You may see that if we project the whole graph on a sphere as indicated in Section 8.1 there is really no distinction between the infinite face and the others.

Let us illustrate our discussion by the graph in Figure 8.2.1. Here we have a graph with 10 faces numbered I to X. For instance, Face I has a boundary circuit consisting of the edges

$$(1, 2), \ (2, 11), \ (11, 10), \ (10, 1)$$

while Face VIII is bounded only by the two edges joining the vertices 10 and 12. The maximal circuit C_1 has edges which run through the vertices 1 to 10 in order and then back to 1. The infinite face X is the set of all points outside of C_1.

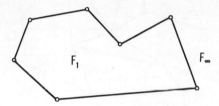

Figure 8.2.2

For polyhedra in space there exists an interesting relation first derived by Euler; it is commonly known as *Euler's polyhedral formula*. It is valid also for our polygonal graphs. In such a graph G we denote by

$$\nu_v, \quad \nu_e, \quad \nu_f$$

the number of vertices, edges and faces, respectively, of G.

Then Euler's formula states:

(8.2.1) $\nu_v - \nu_e + \nu_f = 2.$

PROOF. The formula is valid in the simplest case where we have only one polygon consisting of n edges (Figure 8.2.2). In this case

$$\nu_v = \nu_e = n, \qquad \nu_f = 2,$$

and so (8.2.1) holds. We shall use mathematical induction to prove the relation in general. We shall show that if it holds for graphs with ν_f faces, then it also holds for graphs with $\nu_f + 1$ faces. Polygonal graphs can be constructed stepwise; in each step a face is added on the "outside".

Suppose that G (the solid part in Figure 8.2.3) is a polygonal graph with ν_v vertices, ν_e edges and ν_f faces, and that the numbers ν_v, ν_e and ν_f satisfy Euler's formula. We add a new face as indicated (see the dashed lines in Figure 8.2.3) by drawing an arc of edges through F_∞ connecting two vertices on the maximal circuit of G. If this arc has r edges we have added $r - 1$ new vertices and one new face. But then it is clear that Euler's relation remains valid for the augmented graph, since

$$\nu_v - \nu_e + \nu_f = (\nu_v + r - 1) - (\nu_e + r) + (\nu_f + 1).$$

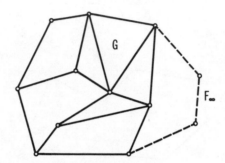

Figure 8.2.3

Problem Set 8.2

1. Verify Euler's formula for the graph in Figure 1.4.1.

2. Do the same for the graph formed by the 8×8 squares of a chess board. Generalize to a board with $n \times n$ squares.

8.3 Graph Relations. Dual Graphs

We shall assume from now on that we deal with polygonal graphs. We write Euler's formula (8.2.1) in the form

(8.3.1) $$\nu_v + \nu_f = \nu_e + 2.$$

The number of edges of a graph can be obtained by counting the edges at each vertex. Since each edge is counted twice in this manner, we find the expression

(8.3.2) $$2\nu_e = \rho(A_1) + \cdots + \rho(A_n), \qquad n = \nu_v,$$

just as in (1.6.1); here $\rho(A_i)$ is the local degree, that is, the number of edges at the vertex A_i. For the graph in Figure 8.2.1 one finds $\nu_e = 22$.

There is another way of counting the edges of a polygonal graph. For a given graph G, let φ_k denote the number of faces in G bounded by k edges. For example, the graph in Figure 8.2.1 has

$$\varphi_2 = 1, \ \varphi_3 = 3, \ \varphi_4 = 3, \ \varphi_5 = 1, \ \varphi_6 = 1, \ \varphi_7 = 0, \ \varphi_8 = 0, \ \varphi_9 = 0, \ \varphi_{10} = 1.$$

In other words, among its 10 faces there is one bounded by two edges, there are three bounded by three edges, and so on.

Since there are no loops in these polygonal nets, there are no faces bounded by only one edge. We therefore have the relation

$$(8.3.3) \qquad \qquad \nu_f = \varphi_2 + \varphi_3 + \varphi_4 + \cdots.$$

Now to count the edges in the graph we notice that each edge lies on the boundary of just two faces, and so we arrive at the formula

$$(8.3.4) \qquad \qquad 2\nu_e = 2\varphi_2 + 3\varphi_3 + 4\varphi_4 + \cdots.$$

In the example in Figure 8.2.1 we obtain $\nu_e = 22$ as before.

For any polygonal graph G one can construct a new polygonal graph G^*, its *dual graph*, by the following method: Within each face, including the infinite face, one selects a single point. Two such inner points A and B are then connected by an edge in case they belong to neighboring faces with a common boundary edge E, and the new edge from A to B is drawn so that it crosses E but no other edges of the graph. If there are several boundary edges common to the two faces, one new edge is drawn for each. We have illustrated the situation in Figure 8.3.1, where G consists of solid lines and G^* of dashed lines.

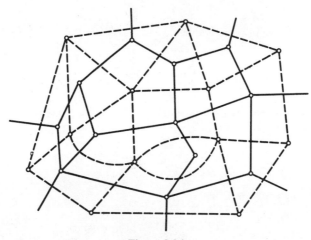

Figure 8.3.1

The dual graph G^* is of importance in the study of planar graphs; indeed, such dual graphs can be defined only for planar graphs.

The dual graph of a polygonal graph is itself a polygonal graph. One sees from Figure 8.3.1 that to each face F of the graph G there corresponds exactly one vertex V^* of the graph G^*, and the number of edges at a vertex V^* in G^* is the same as the number of boundary edges of the corresponding face F in G. This shows that the local degree of V^* in G^* is the number of boundary edges of the corresponding face of F in G. Each edge E in G corresponds to a unique edge E^* crossing it in G^*.

At each vertex V in G there are $\rho(V)$ edges. Each of these is crossed by an edge of G^* and these edges form a face F^* of G^*. Therefore, there are $\rho(V)$ edges of G^* on the boundary of F^*. From the figure one also sees that G is the dual of G^*. The two graphs have the same number of edges; the number of vertices in G^* is the number of faces in G and the number of faces in G^* is the number of vertices in G.

8.4 The Platonic Bodies

We said that a graph was regular (Section 1.6) if the number ρ of edges was the same at each vertex. For a polygonal graph G we shall say that it is *completely regular* if also the dual graph G^* is regular. This means (see the preceding section) that each face in G shall be bounded by the same number of edges, say ρ^*.

There are, as we shall show, very few completely regular graphs. If we count the number of edges in G as in (8.3.2) and (8.3.4) we find, in the case of completely regular graphs, that these expressions reduce to

$$(8.4.1) \qquad 2\nu_e = \rho\nu_v = \rho^*\nu_f.$$

From (8.4.1) we take the values

$$\nu_e = \frac{1}{2}\rho\,\nu_v, \qquad \nu_f = \frac{\rho}{\rho^*}\,\nu_v$$

and substitute into Euler's formula (8.3.1). This gives the result

$$\nu_v\!\left(1 + \frac{\rho}{\rho^*} - \frac{1}{2}\rho\right) = 2$$

which we can represent as

$$(8.4.2) \qquad \nu_v(2\rho + 2\rho^* - \rho\rho^*) = 4\rho^*.$$

Since ν_v and ρ^* are positive integers the expression in parentheses must also be a positive integer:

$$2\rho + 2\rho^* - \rho\rho^* > 0.$$

This latter condition we prefer to rewrite as $\rho\rho^* - 2\rho - 2\rho^* < 0$, or

(8.4.3) $(\rho - 2)(\rho^* - 2) < 4.$

We shall solve the inequality (8.4.3) in two steps. First, consider the case that both factors, $\rho - 2$ and $\rho^* - 2$, are positive; that is, ρ and ρ^* are greater than 2. Since the only pairs of positive integers with a product less than 4 are 1 and 1, 1 and 2, and 1 and 3, we see that $\rho - 2 < 3$ and $\rho^* - 2 < 3$. In this case the only 5 possible values ρ and ρ^* can take are listed in the table of Figure 8.4.1.

Completely regular graphs

ρ	ρ^*	ν_v	ν_e	ν_f	Type
3	3	4	6	4	Tetrahedron
3	4	8	12	6	Cube
3	5	20	30	12	Dodecahedron
4	3	6	12	8	Octahedron
5	3	12	30	20	Icosahedron

Figure 8.4.1

The number of edges, vertices and faces in the table have been computed from the expressions (8.4.1) and (8.4.2). In constructing the completely regular graphs listed in the table one would begin with a triangle, quadrangle, pentagon according as the value of ρ^* is 3, 4 or 5. By fitting the polygons together so that the right number of faces meet at each vertex one sees that there is exactly one isomorphic type (drawn in Figure 8.4.2) of complete regular graphs for each of the five sets of values.

The dual of a completely regular graph is, by definition, also completely regular. From our table we see that the octahedron graph is dual to the cube, the icosahedron to the dodecahedron, while the tetrahedron is its own dual.

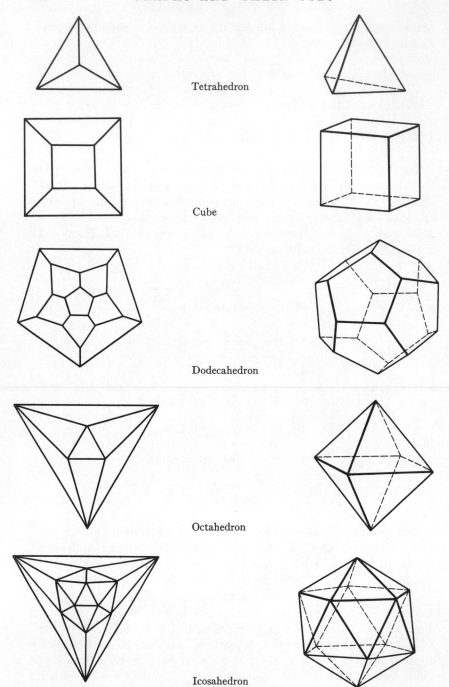

Tetrahedron

Cube

Dodecahedron

Octahedron

Icosahedron

Figure 8.4.2

In finding positive integers ρ and ρ^* satisfying the condition (8.4.3) we first considered values $\rho > 2$ and $\rho^* > 2$ and were led to the tabulated results. But this inequality also has solutions when ρ (or ρ^*) takes on the value 2 or 1. The corresponding graphs turn out to be quite trivial.

If $\rho = 2$ we have a connected graph with two edges at each vertex, in short, a circuit (Figure 8.4.3). If $\rho^* = 2$, then (8.4.2) becomes

$$\nu_v(2\rho + 4 - 2\rho) = 4\nu_v = 8$$

so that $\nu_v = 2$; the graph therefore consists of two vertices connected by a number of edges (Figure 8.4.4). Observe that the dual of a circuit with two faces, n vertices and n edges has two vertices, n faces and n edges. In other words, the dual of a graph of the type pictured in Figure 8.4.3 is of the type pictured in Figure 8.4.4.

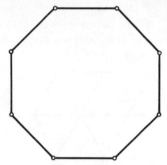
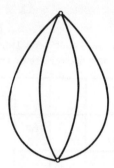

Figure 8.4.3   Figure 8.4.4

When $\rho = 1$ the inequality (8.4.3) is satisfied for any positive value of ρ^*. (Check it!) But a connected graph with only one edge at each vertex must consist of a single edge; that is, it must have

$$\nu_v = 2, \quad \nu_e = \nu_f = 1, \qquad \rho = 1, \quad \rho^* = 2.$$

You may verify that, when $\rho^* = 1$, the graph is a single loop with the dual set of values

$$\nu_v = \nu_e = 1, \quad \nu_f = 2, \qquad \rho = 2, \quad \rho^* = 1.$$

In the 13th book of Euclid's Elements one finds a discussion of the *regular polyhedra*. These bodies are inscribed in a sphere, all boundary faces are regular and congruent polygons, and at each vertex there is the same number of adjoining side edges and faces. The graph of such a polyhedron defined by its corners and side edges is completely regular; it is planar because it can be projected upon the sphere from its center.

Plato mentioned the regular polyhedra in *Timaeus* and such was his influence that they have ever since been known as the Platonic bodies. Nor was Euclid the discoverer of these polyhedra; they were known to some of his predecessors, some even to the Pythagoreans. Throughout Antiquity and the Middle Ages the Platonic bodies were considered to be symbols of the harmony of the universe.

It follows from our discussion of completely regular graphs that there can be no Platonic bodies other than the five sketched in Figure 8.4.2.

Problem Set 8.4

1. Draw the duals of the tetrahedron, the cube and the octahedron.

2. Do the regular polyhedra have Hamilton lines?

8.5 Mosaics

When you look upon a bathroom floor you are apt to see a pattern of regular polygons repeating itself. The shape of the polygons may vary; there may be squares or triangles or hexagons (Figure 8.5.1).

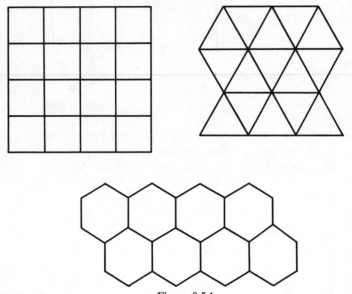

Figure 8.5.1

These patterns for mosaic floors have been popular since early antiquity. In nature one finds many instances of such repeated patterns with similar, if not congruent units. In botany they are studied under the heading of phyllotaxis, the arrangement of buds and seeds in plants;

you may be familiar with such regularities from the pattern on a pine-apple or the arrangements of the seeds in a sunflower.

From a general point of view, we may say that we have a planar graph in which faces with the same number of edges are repeated a large number of times. We shall show again that there is only a small number of patterns which are actually possible.

Let us use the same notation as before: There are ρ edges at each vertex and each face has ρ^* boundary edges. We begin our mosaic with one of these faces and add others to it until a certain part of the plane is covered, just as a floor is usually laid.

We now have a polygonal graph G in which all faces but the infinite face are bounded by ρ^* edges and there are ρ edges at each vertex except at those on the boundary of F_∞.

We suppose that we lay our mosaic in such a manner that when the number of pieces increases the proportion of the number ν_b of vertices on the boundary to the total number ν_v of vertices becomes smaller and smaller. In the usual limit terminology this is expressed symbolically as

$$(8.5.1) \qquad \frac{\nu_b}{\nu_v} \to 0 \qquad \text{as} \qquad \nu_v \to \infty\, ;$$

in words: the ratio ν_b/ν_v approaches zero as ν_v approaches infinity.

Let us estimate the number of edges in G by counting them at each vertex as in the formula (8.3.2). If we are generous and count ρ edges at each vertex we obtain $\rho\nu_v$ of them. On the other hand if we omit the edges at all ν_b vertices on the boundary we obtain $\rho(\nu_v - \nu_b)$ edges. Thus we know that

$$\rho\nu_v - \rho\nu_b < 2\nu_e < \rho\nu_v\, ,$$

where ν_e is the number of edges in G. We can rewrite these inequalities in the form

$$\frac{\rho}{2} - \frac{\rho}{2}\frac{\nu_b}{\nu_v} < \frac{\nu_e}{\nu_v} < \frac{\rho}{2}\, .$$

From (8.5.1) we conclude that

$$(8.5.2) \qquad \frac{\nu_e}{\nu_v} \to \frac{\rho}{2} \qquad \text{as} \qquad \nu_v \to \infty\, .$$

Next let us count the edges by means of the faces as in the formula (8.3.4). There are $\nu_f - 1$ faces with ρ^* boundary edges, and the face F_∞ has ν_b boundary edges, the same as the number of boundary vertices.

From this we conclude that

$$2\nu_e = (\nu_f - 1)\rho^* + \nu_b;$$

we divide both sides of this expression by ν_v and ρ^*, and then bring it into the form

$$\frac{\nu_f}{\nu_v} = \frac{2}{\rho^*}\frac{\nu_e}{\nu_v} + \frac{1}{\nu_v} - \frac{1}{\rho^*}\frac{\nu_b}{\nu_v}.$$

When $\nu_v \to \infty$, the two last terms on the right tend to zero, and so from (8.5.2) we conclude that

$$(8.5.3)\qquad \frac{\nu_f}{\nu_v} \to \frac{2}{\rho^*}\frac{\rho}{2} = \frac{\rho}{\rho^*} \qquad \text{as} \qquad \nu_v \to \infty.$$

Let us turn back to Euler's formula (8.3.1), now written in the form

$$1 + \frac{\nu_f}{\nu_v} = \frac{\nu_e}{\nu_v} + \frac{2}{\nu_v}.$$

For large ν_v the left-hand side tends to

$$1 + \frac{\rho}{\rho^*}$$

according to (8.5.3), while the right-hand side tends to $\frac{1}{2}\rho$ according to (8.5.2). Both sides must tend to the same limit and we conclude that

$$1 + \frac{\rho}{\rho^*} = \frac{\rho}{2},$$

and this condition we finally rewrite as

$$(\rho - 2)(\rho^* - 2) = 4.$$

The only pairs of integers that can satisfy this equation are

$$\rho = 3, \quad \rho^* = 6; \qquad \rho = 4, \quad \rho^* = 4; \qquad \rho = 6, \quad \rho^* = 3.$$

We conclude that all repetitive planar graph patterns or mosaics must be formed either by triangles, or by quadrangles, or by hexagons. All three of these are illustrated in Figure 8.5.1.

CHAPTER NINE

Map Coloring

9.1 The Four Color Conjecture

When we have a polygonal map before us we may think of the faces as being countries or states on a map with the ocean surrounding them in the form of the infinite face. In a good atlas the countries, together with the ocean, are colored in different colors to distinguish them from each other. This means that the coloring must be done so that countries with a common boundary have different colors. If one has a large number of colors at one's disposal this represents no particular problem. Much more difficult is the question of finding the smallest number of colors sufficient for coloring the countries of a given map.

The famous conjecture is that every map can be colored properly by means of four colors. The British mathematician Cayley, himself one of the pioneers in graph theory, in 1879 published an article on the four color problem, appropriately enough in the first volume of the Proceedings of the Royal Geographical Society. One often sees this article referred to as the birth certificate of the four color problem. However, this is not quite correct. The Scottish physicist Frederick Guthrie related that around 1850 it was a well-known problem among the mathematics students in London and that his brother Francis Guthrie brought it to the attention of his mathematics professor De Morgan.

At first the problem does not seem to have been taken too seriously; the mathematicians appear to have considered it a fairly self-evident fact. Later, a number of incorrect proofs appeared; the four color problem, so puzzlingly simple to state, has withstood every assault by some of the world's most capable mathematicians. However, interest in graph theory has been mightily stimulated by the problem; many important graph results have been discovered because they show promise of being helpful for the resolution of the four color conjecture.

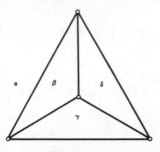

Figure 9.1.1

Let us point out immediately that for some graphs it is essential that we have as many as four colors. As an example we may take the case of the tetrahedron graph (Figure 9.1.1). (In the following we shall always denote the various colors by Greek letters α, β, γ, δ, ϵ, $\cdots$; usually it does not matter which particular color the letters indicate.) For the tetrahedron we may suppose that the infinite face or outer region has the color α. The three other faces then must have different colors, since they all have common boundaries.

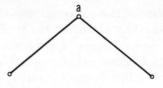

Figure 9.1.2

We observe next that in trying to color a map with as few colors as possible, we need not concern ourselves with vertices where only two edges meet. For, if a is such a vertex one can combine the two edges into one and eliminate the vertex a (Figure 9.1.2) without changing the color scheme in any way.

According to this remark, it suffices to consider graphs where there are at least three edges at each vertex. But we can make a much more radical supposition: The coloring of an arbitrary polygonal graph in a certain number of colors can be reduced to the case where the graph is *regular of degree three*, that is, there are exactly three edges at each vertex.

In other words, if we can solve the coloring problem for regular graphs of degree three, we can solve it for all graphs.

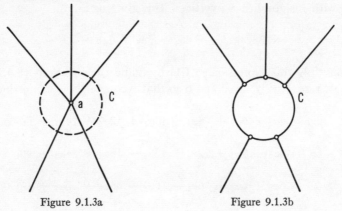

Figure 9.1.3a   Figure 9.1.3b

Suppose that we have more than three edges at some vertex a (Figure 9.1.3a). We draw a small circle C around a so that it does not reach any other vertex. We eliminate a and those parts of its edges which lie inside the circle and replace them by edges consisting of the sections of C (Figure 9.1.3b). All the new vertices will have three edges. Any coloring of the new graph G_1 will produce a coloring for the original graph G when one shrinks the circle C down to a single point. By continued changes of this kind on all vertices with more than three edges we reduce our coloring problem to that of coloring a regular polygonal graph of degree three.

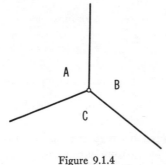

Figure 9.1.4

In the following we shall restrict ourselves to regular graphs of degree three. For these, there is a useful formula in addition to those derived in Section 8.3; it is based on the observation that now each vertex lies on the boundary of exactly three faces (Figure 9.1.4). As a consequence, when we count the number of vertices on all faces we obtain three times the total number of vertices. Previously we denoted by φ_i the number of faces with i edges, hence i vertices. This gives us

$$(9.1.1) \qquad 3\nu_v = 2\varphi_2 + 3\varphi_3 + 4\varphi_4 + 5\varphi_5 + 6\varphi_6 + 7\varphi_7 + \cdots.$$

We multiply this expression (9.1.1) by 2 and the equations (8.3.4) and (8.3.3), respectively, by 3 and 6 so that we have three expressions

$$6\nu_v = 4\varphi_2 + 6\varphi_3 + 8\varphi_4 + 10\varphi_5 + 12\varphi_6 + 14\varphi_7 + \cdots$$

$$6\nu_e = 6\varphi_2 + 9\varphi_3 + 12\varphi_4 + 15\varphi_5 + 18\varphi_6 + 21\varphi_7 + \cdots$$

$$6\nu_f = 6\varphi_2 + 6\varphi_3 + 6\varphi_4 + 6\varphi_5 + 6\varphi_6 + 6\varphi_7 + \cdots.$$

We now rewrite Euler's formula (8.3.1) in the form

$$12 = 6\nu_v - 6\nu_e + 6\nu_f$$

and substitute our values. The result is

$$(9.1.2) \qquad 12 = 4\varphi_2 + 3\varphi_3 + 2\varphi_4 + \varphi_5 - \varphi_7 - 2\varphi_8 - \cdots,$$

where the remaining terms are all negative. Since the right-hand side in (9.1.2) must be positive we conclude:

In a regular graph of degree 3 there must be some faces bounded by less than six edges.

9.2 The Five Color Theorem

In the following we shall examine the possibility of coloring a graph in four or five colors; according to the preceding remarks we can assume that we deal with a polygonal regular graph G of degree 3, and we know that such a graph has at least one face bounded by fewer than six edges.

In what follows, we shall deal separately with faces bounded by 2, 3, 4 and 5 edges. In each case we shall show (a) that some boundaries can be deleted so that the resulting graph is again regular of degree three but has fewer faces and (b) that if the reduced graph can be colored with no more than five colors, then this can be done for the original graph as well. Since our reductions always lead to regular graphs of degree three, we

can be sure that after each such simplification, there is again a face
bounded by fewer than six edges and so we are led, successively, to graphs
with fewer and fewer regions to be colored.

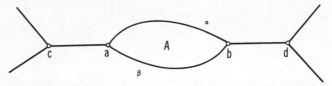

Figure 9.2.1

Multiple edges. (a) Our first step is to show that G can always be simplified so that there are no faces bounded by two edges. If there is a
double edge between a and b as in Figure 9.2.1 then we eliminate one of
them and join the remaining one with the third edges (a, c) and (b, d)
at a and b and replace them by a single edge (c, d). The new graph G_1
is again regular of degree 3.

(b) If G_1 can be colored there will be different colors α and β on the
two sides of the edge (c, d). We can then replace a and b and the double
edge and give the enclosed face A a third color γ.

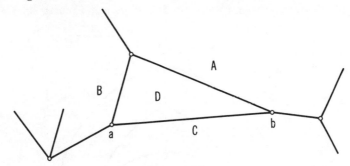

Figure 9.2.2

Triangular faces. (a) The graph can be simplified so that it includes
no triangular faces. Suppose that D is such a face bordering upon three
others A, B, C. Let (a, b) be the boundary edge between C and D (Figure
9.2.2). We eliminate the edge (a, b) and join the two other edges at a
into a single one and similarly at b. The reduced graph G_1 then is regular
of degree 3.

(b) When G_1 has been colored the face A will have a color α, B a color
β and the face $C + D$ a color γ. When the edge (a, b) is restored we
need only to give D a fourth color δ.

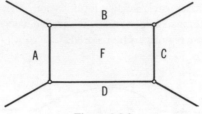

Figure 9.2.3

Quadrilateral faces. (a) It is a little more involved to show that one can eliminate faces with four edges on the border. Let F be such a face with neighboring faces A, B, C, D as in Figure 9.2.3. It is possible that A and C are only different parts of the same face, or it may happen that they have a borderline (m, n) in common as we have indicated in Figure 9.2.4. In either case the face (or faces) $A + C$ cuts B off from any common border with D. We now eliminate the edges (a, b) and (c, d) and join the edges (a_1, a), (a, c), (c, c_1) into a single one (a_1, c_1); similarly we combine (b_1, b), (b, d), (d, d_1) into a single edge (b_1, d_1). Then the new graph G_1 is regular of degree 3 and $B + F + D$ is a single face.

(b) Suppose that G_1 has been colored and $B + F + D$ has the color α. Then A and C have colors β and γ, possibly alike. But then we can restore our two edges (a, b) and (c, d) and give F a fourth color δ.

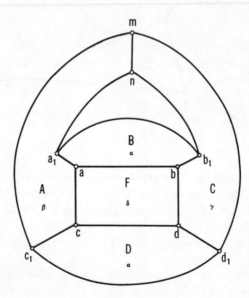

Figure 9.2.4

Pentagonal faces. (a) Suppose we have a face *F* bordering upon five others, *A*, *B*, *C*, *D*, *E*, as in Figure 9.2.5. By the same argument as that given for the quadrilateral we conclude that there is a pair of oppositely located bordering faces to *F*, say *A* and *C*, such that they are not parts of the same face, nor have a common border. We now eliminate the edges (a, b) and (c, d). (See Figure 9.2.5.) Again the graph becomes regular of degree 3 if we eliminate the vertices *a*, *b*, *c*, *d* by joining the two remaining edges to a single one at each of these vertices.

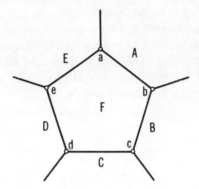

Figure 9.2.5

(b) Suppose we have colored this reduced graph and the face $A + F + C$ has the color α. The three faces *B*, *D*, *E* may require up to three different colors, β, γ, δ. If we have five colors at our disposal we can restore the two edges (a, b) and (c, d) and give *F* a fifth color ε. However, if we have only four colors such a reduction may not always be possible.

We see from this discussion that if the regular graph has faces with 2, 3, 4, 5 edges and there are five colors available, the coloring problem can always be reduced to one involving a graph with a smaller number of faces. The last observation in the preceding section shows that a regular graph has at least one such small face so the reduction can always be continued until the graph has only five or fewer faces and hence can certainly be colored with no more than five colors. We have proved:

FIVE COLOR THEOREM. *A planar graph can always be colored in five colors.*

This argument is not applicable when we have only four colors. As we saw, pentagons cannot be reduced in this case. Our reduction process may come to a halt with some regular graph where each face has at least five boundary edges. Then there are no faces with 2, 3, or 4 boundary edges and we have

$$\varphi_2 = \varphi_3 = \varphi_4 = 0.$$

Formula (9.1.2) shows that such an irreducible regular graph must have at least 12 pentagons. Actually it has been shown that any map with less than 39 faces can be colored in four colors. This is not a very high bound in our age of computers. If one could devise a method of programming the problem for a computer it seems likely that one could push this bound much higher; who knows, one might even encounter a map that cannot be colored in four colors. However, this is improbable; so many special restrictions have been derived for such a map that one has a feeling that it just cannot exist. It would fill another volume to give an account of the many papers on the four color problem so we must rest content in having introduced you to it.

Solutions

Chapter 1

Set 1.1, page 7

2. *AB, AE, AD, BC, BG, BF, CD, CG, DH, EH, EG, EF, FH, FG, GH.*

3. 9 edges, 6 vertices; 15 edges, 8 vertices.

Set 1.2, page 9

1.

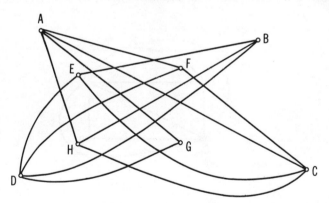

2. $\frac{1}{2}n(n - 1)$

Set 1.3, page 12

1. Graph 1.1.1 is not isomorphic to graph 1.1.2, for the latter has a vertex *G* with 5 edges and there is no such vertex in 1.1.1. Also 1.1.1 is not isomorphic to 1.2.4, for the latter has a vertex *F* with only one edge; for the same reason 1.1.2 and 1.2.4 are not isomorphic.

2. The edge $(5, 8)$ in the first graph belongs to two circuits of length 4 and there is no such edge in the second graph.

3. When the vertices correspond as in the figure then the edges correspond.

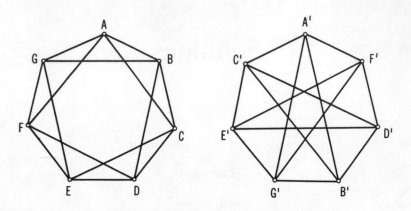

Set 1.5, page 17

1. and 2. The four original neighbors may be A, B, C, D, and their roads form a planar graph as in the figure. Wherever the fifth point E is placed it is always separated from one of the others by a closed circuit.

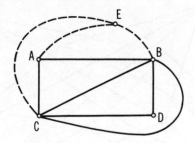

Set 1.6, page 20

1. In Figure 1.1.2 one has $\rho(A) = \rho(C) = \rho(D) = 3$,

$$\rho(B) = \rho(E) = \rho(F) = \rho(H) = 4, \quad \rho(G) = 5,$$

and there are $\frac{1}{2}(3\cdot 3 + 4\cdot 4 + 5) = 15$ edges. In Figure 1.2.4 one has

$$\rho(A) = \rho(B) = \rho(D) = \rho(E) = 2, \quad \rho(C) = 3, \quad \rho(F) = 1,$$

and $\frac{1}{2}(4\cdot 2 + 3 + 1) = 6$ edges.

2. There are respectively 4 and 2 odd vertices.

Chapter 2

Set 2.3, page 27

1. There are two odd vertices in each graph in Figure 2.3.2; hence both graphs can be covered in a single path.

3. The graph U_4 can be covered by the two paths 1, 2, 3, 4 and 2, 4, 1, 3. For U_5 take the single path 1, 2, 3, 4, 5, 1, 4, 2, 5, 3, 1.

Set 2.5, page 30

1. The first graph has the Hamilton line $A\,C\,B\,F\,E\,D\,A$, the second $A\,B\,F\,E\,H\,G\,C\,D\,A$.

2. The shortest path $A_1A_2A_4A_3A_1$ is 470 miles long.

Set 2.6, page 33

1. The number of persons on the second side increases by at most one person at each passage. Thus if the problem were solvable there would at one stage be 5 persons transferred. These cannot consist of 4 women and 1 man, nor of 3 women and 2 men because one woman would be without her husband. Nor can there be 2 women and 3 men because on the other side of the river a woman would be without her husband. The 5 persons transferred must therefore be 1 woman and 4 men. In the last transfer 1 woman, 1 man or 2 men must have arrived. Both are impossible. In the first case one man must have been alone with 4 women on the first side; in the second, 2 men would have been there with 3 women.

2. When the pairs are Aa, Bb, Cc, Dd, the transfers can be made in the following stages: (a, b, c), (a, b, c, d), (Aa, Bb, Cc), (Aa, Bb, Cc, D), (Aa, Bb, Cc, Dd).

3. 336 moves when directions are taken into account, 168 otherwise.

4. There are 4 corner positions with 3 moves, 24 side positions with 5 moves and 36 central positions with 8 moves.

Chapter 3

Set 3.2, page 38

1. The circuit ranks of these graphs are respectively
$$\gamma = 15 - 8 + 1 = 8 \quad \text{and} \quad \gamma = 32 - 21 + 1 = 12.$$

2. $\gamma = \frac{1}{2}(n - 1)n - n + 1 = \frac{1}{2}(n - 1)(n - 2)$.

Set 3.4, page 42

1. For the graph in Figure 1.1.1 one has for instance:

$$A \to AC, \quad B \to BE, \quad C \to CB, \quad D \to DA, \quad E \to EF, \quad F \to FA.$$

For the graph in Figure 1.1.2,

$$A \to AB, \quad B \to BC, \quad C \to CD, \quad D \to DA,$$

$$E \to EF, \quad F \to FG, \quad G \to GH, \quad H \to HE.$$

Chapter 4

Set 4.2, page 48

1. A nearly trivial example consists in letting each member be a committee of one. Then no one could serve as chairman of any other committee.

2. The number of committees is

$$\frac{12 \cdot 11 \cdot 10}{1 \cdot 2 \cdot 3} = 220,$$

much larger than the number 12 of possible chairmen.

3. One matching is $m_1 \to p_2$, $m_2 \to p_1$, $m_3 \to p_4$, $m_4 \to p_5$.

Set 4.3, page 52

2. Properties a) and b) are consequences of the fact that each line and column in Figure 4.3.2 includes every number from 1 to N exactly once. To prove statement c), we analyze the construction of the table in Figure 4.3.2. If one counts also the first row and the first column, then one has N rows and N columns whose entries are constructed by the following rule:

(a) In the ith row and ith column, player i faces player 1.
(b) When $i \neq j$, player number j faces, in the ith row, the player whose number is

$$k = 2i - j + [\pm(N - 1)]$$

(where we add or subtract $N - 1$ if necessary to make k lie between 2 and N). If we solve this expression for j we obtain

$$j = 2i - k + [\pm (N - 1)];$$

the symmetric roles played by k and j confirm the assertion made in part c) of the problem.

Chapter 5

Set 5.3, page 62

2. One must write

$$\rho(A) + \rho^*(A) + \rho_0(A) = k, \qquad \rho(B) + \rho^*(B) + \rho_0(B) = k - 1,$$

where $\rho_0(A)$ is the number of draws.

3. For $n = 5$ one has the graph

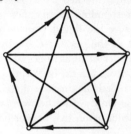

Set 5.4, page 67

1. The graphs are

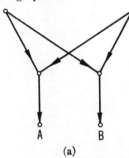 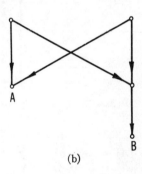

(a)   (b)

2. If 1 is taken to be a male then 2, 7 are females, 5 is male and the other vertices may have an arbitrary sex character.

3.

 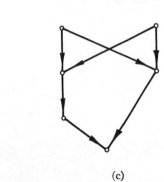

(a)   (b)   (c)

Chapter 6

Set 6.1, page 70

1. and 2. Since the only measuring devices at our disposal are the jugs B and C themselves, we have no way of judging how the liquid is distributed except when one of these jugs is either full or empty. All such distributions of the liquid are represented by points (marked by circles) on the border of the rectangle in the figure below. The set of distributions U is represented by the inner points (marked by x) of this rectangle. Suppose we have a distribution corresponding to an inner point. Then, the only way we can accurately measure the liquid transferred in the next pouring is by either emptying one of the jugs B, C, or by filling one of these jugs. In any case, such a transfer of liquid necessarily leads to a point on the border of the graph. Once we have a full or an empty jug, the next measurable transfer of liquid leads again to a distribution where at least one of the jugs is either full or empty. In other words, each measurable pouring from a border position leads again to a border position, so the inner points U cannot be reached.

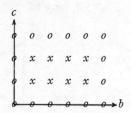

3. $(7, 0)(3, 4)(3, 0)(0, 3)(7, 3)(6, 4)(6, 0)$.

Set 6.2, page 75

2. $W_1(A) = (0, 0, \alpha)$, $\alpha \geq 1$; $L_1(B) = (1, 1, 0)$;
$W_2(A) = (0, 0, \alpha)$, $(1, 1, \beta)$, $(0, 1, \gamma)$, $\beta \geq 1$, $\gamma \geq 2$;
$L_2(B) = (1, 1, 0)$, $(0, 2, 2)$.

3. In the figure the O's indicate winning positions for A, the squares losing positions for B.

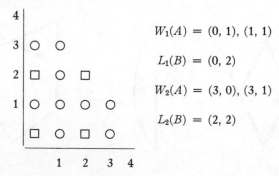

$W_1(A) = (0, 1), (1, 1)$

$L_1(B) = (0, 2)$

$W_2(A) = (3, 0), (3, 1)$

$L_2(B) = (2, 2)$

Set 6.3, page 79

2. The draws must be represented as edges in both directions.

Chapter 7

Set 7.1, page 82

1. Take, for example, the relations "a is greater than the square of b", or "the sets A and B have no common elements", or "a triangle intersects another".

2. a)

R_6: $\{2, 3, 4, 5\}$, R_5: $\{2, 3, 4\}$,
R_4: $\{2, 3\}$, R_3: $\{2\}$, R_2: $\{\varnothing\}$.

b) This relation is represented by the complete graph with 5 vertices without loops; R_6: $\{2, 3, 4, 5\}$, R_5: $\{2, 3, 4, 6\}$, R_4: $\{2, 3, 5, 6\}$, R_3: $\{2, 4, 5, 6\}$, R_2: $\{3, 4, 5, 6\}$.

c)

R_6: $\{6\}$, R_5: $\{5\}$, R_4: $\{4\}$
R_3: $\{3, 6\}$, R_2: $\{4, 6\}$.

Here we have interpreted $a \mid b$ to be reflexive, i.e. every number divides itself; see also solution to Problem 3 of Set 7.4.

Set 7.2, page 86

2. a) This relation is antireflexive, asymmetric and transitive.
   b) This relation is reflexive, symmetric, but not transitive.

Set 7.3, page 89

2. If $a = b + km$ and $c = d + k_1m$,   then
$$a + c = b + d + (k + k_1)m,$$
$$a - c = b - d + (k - k_1)m,$$
and
$$a \cdot c = bd + (dk + bk_1)m + kk_1m^2$$
$$= bd + (dk + bk_1 + kk_1m)m.$$
Therefore $a \pm c \equiv b \pm d \pmod{m}$ and $ac \equiv bd \pmod{m}$.

3. The relation $\mid a \mid = \mid b \mid$ for numbers a, b is reflexive, symmetric, and transitive, so it is an equivalence relation. Each equivalence block consists of the pair $(a, -a)$ and the members of each pair are distinct except when $a = 0$.

Set 7.4, page 93

1. In the complete order graph, we have the edges (4, 3), (4, 2), (4, 1), (3, 2), (3, 1), (2, 1); the basis graph is the directed arc 4321.

2. The basis graph is a directed arc

3. To show that $a \mid b$ is a partial order, we note first that $a \mid a$ since $a = 1 \cdot a$. [For a strict partial order, we require for $a \mid b$ that $b = k \cdot a$ with $k \neq 1$; in other words, if a must be a proper divisor of b in the relation $a \mid b$, then we deal with an antireflexive relation.] Next, we verify that the relation is transitive: From $a \mid b$ and $b \mid c$, we have $b = ka$ and $c = k_1 b$ so that $c = k_1 ka$, and hence $c \mid a$. Finally, if $a \mid b$ and $b \mid a$, then $b = ka$, $a = lb$, so $b = klb$; this can hold only if the integers k and l have the value 1, i.e. if $a = b$. In the strict partial order, $a \mid b$ and $b \mid a$ cannot both be admitted.

4. There are 8 subsets including $\varnothing$. The basis graph is drawn here; observe that the converse graph is isomorphic to the basis graph.

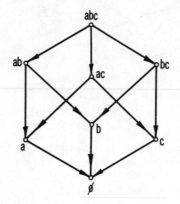

Chapter 8

Set 8.1, page 97

1.

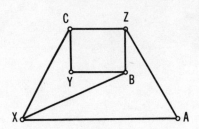

2. They consist of the graph in Figure 8.1.1 and all the graphs which can be obtained by adding edges.

Set 8.2, page 100

1. $\nu_v = 7$, $\nu_e = 11$, $\nu_f = 6$, and $7 - 11 + 6 = 2$.

2. In general: $\nu_v = (n + 1)^2$, $\nu_e = 2n(n + 1)$, $\nu_f = n^2 + 1$, and $\nu_v - \nu_e + \nu_f = 2$.

Set 8.4, page 106

2. Yes.

BIBLIOGRAPHY

The number of books on graph theory is very small.

Avondo–Bodino, G., *Economic Applications of the Theory of Graphs*, New York: Gordon and Breach, 1962.

Franklin, P., *The Four Color Problem*, New York: Scripta Mathematica, Yeshiva University, 1961.

Ore, O., *Theory of Graphs*, Providence, Rhode Island: American Mathematical Society Colloquium Publications, Volume XXXVIII, 1962.

There is a considerable number of applications of graphs to puzzles and games in

Rouse Ball, W., *Mathematical Recreations and Essays*, London and New York: 1892 and MacMillan, 1962.

Foreign works:

Berge, C., *Théorie des graphes et ses applications*, Paris: Dunod, 1958.

Dynkin, E. B. and Uspenski, W. A., *Mathematische Unterhaltungen*: *Mehrfarbenprobleme*, Moscow and Berlin: 1952 and 1955.

König, D., *Theorie der endlichen und unendlichen Graphen*, Leipzig: 1936.

Ringel, G., *Färbungsprobleme auf Flächen und Graphen*, Berlin: 1959.

Sainte-Laguë, A., *Les réseaux (ou graphes)*, Mémorial des Sciences Mathématiques, Volume 18, Paris: 1926.

GLOSSARY

arc. A route in a graph that goes through no vertex more than once.

bridge. Another term for "separating edge".

circuit. An arc that returns to its starting point, i.e. a route that revisits only the beginning vertex.

    maximal circuit C_1 of a polygonal graph G. The circuit which surrounds the whole graph G.

    minimal circuit of a polygonal graph G. A circuit formed by the boundary edges of one of the polygons that compose G.

circuit rank γ of a graph G. Number of edges of G minus the number of vertices of G plus one.

complement $\bar{G}$ of a graph G. $\bar{G}$ consists of all edges (and their endpoints) needed to make a complete graph out of G.

connected component of a vertex A. All vertices reachable from A by arcs in the graph and all edges incident on these vertices.

cyclomatic number. Another term for "circuit rank".

edge. A piece of curve connecting two vertices of a graph and containing no other vertex.

    circuit edge. An edge that is not a separating edge.

    multiple edges. If two vertices of a graph are connected by more than one edge, each such edge is called a multiple edge.

    separating edge. An edge whose removal would result in increasing the number of connected components of the graph.

dodecahedron. A polyhedron of twenty faces.

129

Euler line. A cyclic path that covers every edge of a graph.

face of a polygonal graph. A face of a polygonal graph G is a part of the plane bounded by a minimal circuit of G, or by G's maximal circuit C_1. The face of G with C_1 as boundary is the part of the plane lying outside of C_1; it is called the infinite face.

graph. A figure consisting of points (called vertices) and segments connecting some of these vertices. (The connecting segments may be straight line segments or curved segments and are called edges.)

bipartite graph. A graph whose vertices are divided into non-overlapping sets so that vertices in the same set are not connected by edges.

complete graph. A graph of n vertices with edges connecting all pairs of vertices, i.e. with $\frac{1}{2}n(n-1)$ edges.

completely regular graph. A polygonal regular graph G whose dual graph G^* is also regular.

connected graph. A graph in which every vertex is connected to every other vertex by some arc.

converse graph. G^* of a directed graph G. G^* is the graph obtained from G by reversing the directions of all edges.

directed graph. A graph with directed edges.

dual graph G^* of a polygonal graph G. G^* is a polygonal graph each of whose vertices corresponds to a face of G and each of whose faces corresponds to a vertex of G. Two vertices in G^* are connected by an edge if the corresponding faces in G have a boundary edge in common.

Euler graph. A graph containing an Euler line.

forest. A graph all of whose connected components are trees. (A graph without circuits.)

mixed graph. A graph with some directed and some undirected edges.

null graph. A graph consisting only of isolated vertices; a graph having no edges.

planar graph. A graph that can be drawn in the plane so that its edges intersect only in vertices of the graph.

polygonal graph. A planar graph whose edges form a polygonal net in the plane in such a way that no polygon completely surrounds another.

regular graph of degree r. If all local degrees of a graph are the same, say r, then the graph is called regular of degree r. (In case of directed graphs it is required that both local degrees, ρ and ρ^*, be the same at each vertex and equal to each other.)

tree. A connected graph without circuits.

universal graph. Another term for "complete graph".

Hamilton line. A circuit that covers all vertices of a graph.

isomorphic graphs. G_1 and G_2 are isomorphic if a one to one correspondence can be established between the vertices of G_1 and those of G_2 in such a way that pairs of vertices of G_1 are connected by an edge if and only if the corresponding pairs of vertices of G_2 are connected by an edge. (In case of directed graphs, this correspondence must preserve the direction of edges.)

local degree at A, $\rho(A)$. The number of edges at the vertex A. In case of directed graphs, $\rho(A)$ denotes the number of outgoing edges, $\rho^*(A)$ the number of incoming edges, i.e. there are two local degrees.

path. A route in a graph that goes through no edge more than once.

    circular path. Another term for "cyclic path".

    cyclic path. A path that returns to its starting point.

polygonal net. A set of adjoining polygons in the plane, dividing the plane into polygonal pieces. (The edges of these polygons are not necessarily straight lines.)

polyhedron. A three dimensional figure whose boundary consists of planes.

    regular polyhedron. A polyhedron all of whose faces are congruent polygons and at each of whose corners the same number of polygons meet.

root of a tree. Any vertex that we choose to single out as starting point in a tree.

vertex. Either an endpoint of an edge or an isolated point of a graph.

    even vertex. A vertex with even local degree.

    isolated vertex. A vertex at which there is no edge.

    odd vertex. A vertex with odd local degree.